STUDY GUIDE

D. B. Kennedy, *Red River Community College*
J. W. Mackintosh, *Red River Community College*
J. A. Rink, *Red River Community College*
Ekaterina Gregory, *College of New Caledonia*
Alan Idiens, *College of New Caledonia*
George Kennedy, *College of New Caledonia*

CANADIAN ECONOMICS
Problems and Policies

Seventh Edition

Brian Lyons
Sheridan College

PEARSON

Prentice
Hall

Toronto

ISBN 0-13-120125-5

Acquisitions Editor: Gary Bennett
Developmental Editor: Meaghan Eley
Production Editor: Jennifer Handel
Production Coordinator: Andrea Falkenberg

1 2 3 4 5   08 07 06 05 04

Printed and bound in Canada.

Table of Contents

Microeconomics

Macroeconomics

To the student

The purpose of this study guide and workbook is to assist you in learning the material in the economics text which the guide accompanies. Since each chapter of the text contains a summary and a listing of important terms, there is no reason to repeat them here. However, this study guide does contain a brief review of the central theme of each chapter, together with some of the more difficult concepts.

This study guide contains numerous specific learning objectives which match the written material in the text and the corresponding self-test questions in this guide. If you prepare answers to these objectives, you will have a stronger understanding of the material.

The self-tests are an important component of this study guide. By doing the self-tests, you can check your understanding of the basic concepts in each chapter. The self-tests consist of various types of questions (true-false, multiple-choice, fill-in-the-blanks, short written answers, problems and case studies). While doing the self-tests allows you to check your understanding of the basics of each chapter, you should also refer back to the specific learning objectives of each chapter, and assure yourself that you are able to demonstrate the level of comprehension demanded of you in any of the objectives in this guide.

To make the most effective use of the text and this study guide, the following approach is suggested:

(i)   Read the chapter in the text, including the definitions of new terms and the summary, making notes or highlighting key sections as you wish. You will notice as you use the text that the key terms have already been highlighted for you. This highlighting provides a convenient guide to the main ideas of a chapter. This study guide does not test you in detail on the many new terms that you will be exposed to throughout the text. You are expected to master these terms on your own.

(ii)   Read the review of the chapter in the study guide.

(iii)   Do the study guide's self-test questions for that chapter, checking the answers for correctness and referring back to the text when necessary.

(iv)   Prepare responses to the learning objectives in the study guide, again referring back to the text as necessary.

(v)   Prepare answers to the questions at the end of each chapter in the text.

Micro Chapter 1

WHAT IS ECONOMICS?

This chapter deals with introductory matters such as the definition of economics and the nature of the subject, which ranges from technical analysis to value judgements concerning practical policy choices, to broad philosophical issues. It points out that much so-called economic knowledge consists largely of myths, and that an important objective of introductory economics courses is to replace these myths with logical economic analysis. While such economic analysis does not automatically make policy decisions for government, it clarifies the economic consequences of each policy choice under consideration, and thus assists in the decision-making process. For purposes of studying economics, the subject is divided into two sections: macroeconomics, which deals with the overall operation of the economy, and microeconomics, which focuses on particular aspects of the economic system.

Human wants are endless. Resources available to any society for satisfying human wants are limited or scarce. For these two reasons no society, no matter how rich, is capable of fulfilling all the material wants of its people. This is the essence of the economic problem: *scarcity*. No simple solution exists for this problem. However, some economists have suggested that it is just a matter of increasing efficiency, using resources more fully, acquiring more resources, or limiting our wants.

The economic problem of scarcity gives rise to three important issues facing any economy: what goods to produce, how to produce them and for whom to produce. Answers to these questions demand that choices be made by society. Such choices often involve "opportunity costs."

General Learning Objectives

Consider the scope, the purpose, and the approaches to the study of economics.

Recognize the finite nature of any society's resources, along with the infinite nature of human wants, as being the fundamental economic problem.

Specific Learning Objectives

		Self-Test Reference
1.	Develop a definition of economics	#1,2
2.	Examine some of the myths related to economic reality	#3
3.	Consider the limitations of economic analysis	#4-6
4.	Distinguish between "micro" and "macro" economics	#7,8
5.	Identify the three types of resources and their characteristics	#9-14
6.	Recognize the economic problems	#15-19
7.	Illustrate the economic problem by use of a production-possibilities curve	#23
8.	Develop the concept of "opportunity cost"	#20, 24
9.	Distinguish between economic effectiveness and efficiency	# 22
10.	Examine the role of an economic system in developing answers to the three basic economic questions	#21
11.	Apply the concept of opportunity cost to a business problem	#25
12.	Review the key terms used in the chapter	#26

Self-Test

1. Economics, as the term is used in its broadest sense, deals with

    (a) decisions made by society concerning the production of goods.

    (b) decisions made by society concerning the distribution of goods.

    (c) how a society satisfies the material needs and wants of its people.

    (d) all of the above.

2.   Economics (is/is not) a precise science like mathematics because _____

3.   Identify which of the following statements are TRUE and which are FALSE with respect to Canada's economy:

_____1.   Poverty would be eliminated if only the minimum wage rate were increased.

_____2.   Even the most carefully thought out government policies could not eliminate unemployment and inflation.

_____3.   Lower interest rates would reduce the level of inflation.

_____4.   A balanced government budget is always desirable.

_____5.   A lower international value for the Canadian dollar would damage our economy.

4.   Which is correct? Economic analysis of a policy issue:

(a)   will provide the government with a decision as to which policy choice is best.

(b)   will help to clarify the economic consequences of various policies and improve the basis for decision making.

5.   **TRUE or FALSE?** The disagreement which is so common among economists shows that the field of economics is so inconclusive and contradictory that the analysis and recommendations of economists cannot be taken seriously.

6.   **TRUE or FALSE?** The study of economics emphasizes "what ought to be" rather than "what is" or "what could be." Explain.

_____

_____

_____

_____

7.   "Macroeconomics" deals with _____

_____

_____

8.   "Microeconomics" deals with _____

_____

_____

9.   Besides the physical ability to do work, the labour input includes _____

       _____

10.   Capital equipment is particularly important because _____

       _____

11.   Increases in "output per worker" are defined as increases in _____

       _____

12.   The land resource includes
       (a)   any product manufactured from a natural element such as iron.
       (b)   forests, fields and streams.
       (c)   energy sources provided by nature.
       (d)   (b) and (c) above.

13.   In a "resource rich" country such as Canada
       (a)   land provides such an unlimited supply of materials that it could not be
              described as "scarce."
       (b)   labour is abundant, rather than scarce, as is demonstrated by the high
              unemployment figures.
       (c)   capital is the most abundant of all three resources.
       (d)   all resources would still be described by economists as being "scarce."

14.   While some of the earth's resources become depleted, other resources are being
       created through _____. One example is _____.

15.   Basic human needs (i.e., those material things necessary to sustain life) are
       (a)   limited.   (c)   abundant.
       (b)   infinite.   (d)   scarce.

16.   Human wants are
       (a)   endless, since people everywhere appear to desire more goods than are
              available.
       (b)   limited, due to the finite nature of resources.
       (c)   always short of what society is capable of producing.
       (d)   proportionate to human needs.

17.   What is meant by the statement that every economic system (such as socialism, capitalism, communism) faces the fact of scarcity?

(a)   All economies have depressions during which scarcities exist.

(b)   There are times when some products can be had only by paying high prices.

(c)   There are insufficient productive resources to satisfy all the wants of a society's people.

(d)   In the beginning, every society faces shortages, but a mature economy such as our own overcomes scarcity in time.

(e)   None of the above.

18.   The economic problem facing any society would be less serious if

(a)   human wants were limited.

(b)   resources were more abundant.

(c)   technology advanced at a more rapid pace.

(d)   all of the above.

19.   The "what" problem in economics means that

(a)   goods and services should be produced as efficiently as possible.

(b)   economists have a responsibility to tell us what goods to produce.

(c)   every society should produce only those goods which it can produce most efficiently.

(d)   government must direct our productive efforts.

(e)   every society must in some way decide what goods it will produce (and not produce).

20.   The choice made by politicians to spend on hospital construction instead of helicopters is an example of the concept of

_____.

21.   "How to produce" would not be a problem for society if

(a)   technology were to improve in all areas.

(b)   natural resources were in no danger of being depleted.

(c)   only one mix of inputs were possible in the production of any product.

(d)   all resources were equally scarce.

5

22.   If an economy meets its economic objectives, it is _____ (efficient, effective). When an economy becomes more productive (i.e. achieves higher levels of output per person), it is _____ (efficient, effective).

23.   Assume that the following production possibilities apply to countries I and II.

	Capital Goods	Consumer Goods
A	0	20
B	1	19
C	2	17
D	3	14
E	4	9
F	5	0

Country I operates at point B whereas country II is at point E.

(a)   Which country has the best opportunity for future growth?

(b)   Why?

24.   Susan, age 19, has just graduated from high school and has a full time job offer as cashier at a grocery store paying $19 000 net a year with benefits, estimated value $1 000 a year. Susan is living at home with her parents and contributes $300 a month to household expenses. She owns a car with annual operating costs of $1,500.

Susan is thinking of pursuing a certificate in business at a local college. This would take one year of full-time study. Tuition would be $2 000, books and materials $5 000. She would continue to live at home and own her car.

What is the opportunity cost of Susan of going to college over the next year?

25.   Bob Shaftoe, a small regional retailer, wanted to expand his business interests, so he decided to acquire a manufacturing enterprise from one of his local suppliers. He reasoned that if he could fully employ the business' existing resources he would be able to produce one or a combination of two products for his customers according to the following table.

Production Possibilities	Product A	Product B
A	52	0
B	49	8
C	45	15
D	40	21
E	34	26
F	27	30
G	19	33
H	10	35
I	0	36

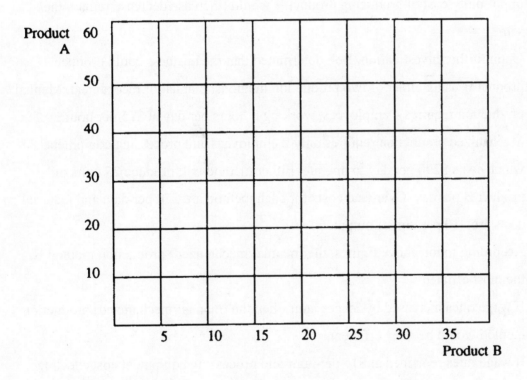

(a)   Sketch the production possibility curve on the above axes.

(b)   If Bob allocated all of the resources of his new business to the production of product A, the business would produce _____ units of A.

(c)   If he chose to produce 26 units of product B, the business would have to give up producing_____ units of A.

(d)   If the opportunity cost of the first 8 units of B is 3 units of product A, then the opportunity cost of producing the 36th unit of B is _____ units of product A.

(e)   If the business could only produce 26 units of product A and 24 units of product B, Mr. Shaftoe may have reason to conclude that the resources of his business are being _____.

(f)   What change would occur in the production possibilities table if Bob could purchase better machinery, hire more staff, acquire more supplies or increase the productivity of his labour force?

_____

_____

(g)   If Bob could manage a more efficient way of producing more of product A, the opportunity cost of producing product B would (increase/decrease/remain the same).

Upon further investigation, Bob determined that the business could produce product B using either of two production methods: manual or mechanical. Manual production requires 4 employees, working 8 hours per day at $15 per hour. Mechanized production requires only 2 employees and processing equipment which costs $290 per day to operate. Either method will produce 25 units of product B per day. Overhead costs for each method are $70 per day, and material costs are $10 per unit of output.

(h)   According to the above figures, the (manual/mechanized) production method is the most efficient.

(i)   If wage rates increased by $5 per hour, then the (manual/mechanized) production method would be most efficient.

(j)   If wage rates remained at $15 per hour and processing equipment costs declined by $60 per day, then the (manual/mechanized) production method would be most efficient.

(k)   If processing equipment costs increased to $340 per day, then the (manual/mechanized) production method would be most efficient.

(1)   If new processing equipment were purchased that doubled output and increased operating costs by $50 per day, then the (manual/mechanized) production method would be most efficient.

(m)   From the above analysis Bob Shaftoe concluded that the most cost efficient production method depends on _____, _____, and _____.

26.

Economics	A	The economic "problem," that wants tend to be unlimited, but the means of satisfying them are not.
Inputs	B	The cost of producing one thing is something else foregone.
Labour	C	A measure of how well an economy performs in producing what is most needed.
Capital (equipment)	D	The goods and services produced by a society.
Productivity	E	A measure in how well an economy performs in producing at the lowest possible cost.
Standard of living	F	Production possibility frontier, a curve that shows the economy's potential output.
Land	G	The study of the decisions a society makes concerning the production of goods and services and the division of these among its people
Output	H	A measure of economic prosperity.
Scarcity A	I	Economic resources, such as labour, capital equipment and natural resources that are used to produce goods and services.
Opportunity cost B	J	Natural resources used in the production of goods and services.
Effectiveness	K	Output per worker hour, a measure of efficiency.
Efficiency	L	Buildings and equipment (Goods used to produce final goods and services).
PPF	M	Human skills used to produce goods and services.

Micro Chapter 2

CANADA'S ECONOMIC SYSTEM

Chapter 2 describes Canada's economic system, which is referred to as a "mixed free enterprise" system. It is basically a market system, but combines the normal market operations with a significant government sector. As such, Canada's economic system does reflect some aspects of a "command" system. Most of the emphasis of this chapter is placed on the theory of the market economy, demonstrating how a market determines answers to the three economic problems and how it organizes the use of economic resources

General Learning Objective

Determine how a mixed free enterprise economic system resolves the three central economic problems.

Specific Learning Objectives

		Self-Test Reference
1.	Identify the major characteristics of the market economy and evaluate its performance using	#1-9
2.	Define the concept of "profit" and confirm the importance of profit in a market economy	#10-12
3.	Assess the role that "competition" plays in an ideal market economy	#13
4.	Identify the major characteristics of the command economy and assess its performance in terms of effectiveness and efficiency	#14, 15
5.	Recognize the elements of command and market forces in a modern mixed economy	#16-19
6.	Review the key terms used in the chapter	#20

Self-Test

1. In a market system, decisions regarding what to produce are made for the most part by _____

2. The interaction between buyers and sellers in the market for "bananas" results in the establishment of:

    (a) price of bananas but not the quantity traded.

    (b) the quantity of bananas traded, but not the price.

    (c) neither price nor quantity of bananas being traded.

    (d) both price and quantity of bananas being traded.

3. The market type of economic system would correct a shortage of a product by:

    (a) lowering the price of the product and the profits of the business firms causing the shortage.

    (b) lowering the price of the product but increasing profits and output of the product by means of a government subsidy.

    (c) government instructions to producers to increase production of the product.

    (d) raising the price of the product and the profits of its producers.

4. A market system type of economy would correct a surplus (oversupply) of a product by

    _____

    _____

5. In a market system type of economy, decisions regarding how to produce things are made by

    _____

    _____

6.   In a market system type of economy, the "for whom" question is basically decided by

    (a)   the way in which total incomes are divided up among individuals and groups.

    (b)   the marketing departments of businesses.

    (c)   the social status of individuals and groups.

    (d)   the government.

    (e)   economists.

7.   In a market economy professional hockey players typically receive much higher pay than steelworkers, even though steel is a most essential commodity. Why?

    (a)   Hockey players are really entertainers rather than producers.

    (b)   There are fewer professional hockey players than steelworkers.

    (c)   Hockey players are more skilled than persons who get less pay.

    (d)   The demand for hockey players is greater than for steelworkers.

    (e)   Compared to the demand for their services, good hockey players are much scarcer than good steelworkers.

8.   In a market type of economic system, the questions of what to produce, how to produce it, and for whom to produce are basically decided by

    (a)   the government.

    (b)   tradition.

    (c)   the people, working consciously for the social good rather than for their own interests.

    (d)   the free decisions of households and businesses, made out of self-interest.

    (e)   economists.

9.   Which of the following statements regarding the market system type of economy are TRUE, and which are FALSE?

    _____(a)   It is a consumer-oriented production system.

    _____(b)   It provides strong work incentives for people.

    _____(c)   It grows steadily, and is not prone to economic fluctuations and crises, such as recessions or depressions.

    _____(d)   It tends to generate a high material standard of living.

_____(e) It tends to result in an equal distribution of economic benefits among various groups and individuals.

_____(f) Its production methods tend to be less efficient than those of other systems.

_____(g) Private economic power groups are unable to become established and enrich themselves at the expense of less powerful groups.

_____(h) It tends to create economic insecurity, particularly due to periodic increases in unemployment.

10. Generally, manufacturers' after-tax profits per dollar of sales amount to about _____ cents.

11. These after-tax profits are available for two uses:

(a) _____

(b) _____

12. State whether each of the following statements regarding business profits is TRUE or FALSE.

_____(a) They provide strong incentives for businesses to produce what the consumers want.

_____(b) They provide strong incentives for businesses to produce goods and services as efficiently as possible.

_____(c) They are considerably larger than the general public supposes them to be.

_____(d) They are an important source of funds for capital investment, which increases prosperity.

13. Competition is an important element of a market economy since it

(a) results in higher prices and therefore higher profits for business.

(b) allows business to be less responsive to consumer wishes and still be profitable.

(c) results in big budget advertising campaigns by business firms.

(d) promotes efficiency in the use of economic resources and therefore lower prices.

(e) decreases the number of firms in an industry.

14.   In a command economy, the decisions regarding **what** to produce, **how** to produce it, and for **whom** to produce it are basically made by

_____

15.   Describe the problems that result from a command economy's lack of incentives

_____

_____

_____

16.   List three ways in which government gets involved in economic decision making in a mixed economy such as Canada's:

1. _____

2. _____

3. _____

17.   The reason for making income tax progressive is to

(a)   reduce exploitation of workers by business.

(b)   reduce the gap between rich and poor.

(c)   reduce pollution of the environment.

(d)   create economic growth.

18.   A mixed economy means that

(a)   the population is made up of various ethnic groups.

(b)   there is a wide variety of industries.

(c)   some production is of consumer goods and services, some of capital items.

(d)   the basic economic questions are answered partly by people, partly by government.

19.   Identify which sector of the Canadian economy the following goods and services are provided in: private, public federal, public provincial, or public municipal.

(a) retailing_____   (b) libraries_____

(c) restaurant service_____   (d) police_____

(e) garbage collection_____   (f) fire fighting_____

(g) pro hockey_____   (h) national defence_____

(i) plastic surgery_____   (j) car manufacturing_____

20.   Match the definitions on the right with the terms on the left.

	Market system	A	Payments by the government of part of the costs of a service in order to reduce the cost to the user of the service.
	Profits	B	The ability to raise one's prices; usually associated with a dominant or monopolistic position in the market.
	Market power	C	Situations in which the economy is producing considerably less that its potential output, and unemployment is high.
	Recessions	D	An economic system in which economic decisions are made mainly by consumers and privately owned producers, in a decentralized manner.
	Command system	E	A measure of the total value of goods and services produced and incomes earned in a country in one year.
	Subsidies	F	Those funds left from a business after all expenses have been paid.
	Gross Domestic Product (GDP)	G	An economic system in which economic decisions are made mainly by the government in a centralized manner.

Micro Chapter 3

BUSINESS ORGANIZATION IN CANADA

This chapter examines the various forms of business organization that exist in Canada. In the private sector, businesses fall under the categories of sole proprietorships, partnerships, and corporations. In the public sector, government enterprises often take the form of Crown corporations.

Business enterprise can also be identified as small, medium-sized, or large. Although small business may take the form of either proprietorships, partnerships or corporations, all large businesses are incorporated.

The dominance of either small business or large business in a particular industry defines the market structure of that industry. In later chapters we will establish the relationship that exists between market structure and the determination of product prices.

General Learning Objective

Examine the various forms of business organization that exist in the Canadian economy.

Specific Learning Objectives

		Self-Test Reference
1.	Develop the progression of a small business enterprise from a proprietorship to a partnership and a corporation	#1
2.	Assess the advantages and disadvantages of each of the three forms of business organization	#2-5
3.	Determine the extent of small business operations in Canada	#6-10

4. Review the problems faced by small business and the assistance available from the CFIB #11, 12

5. Examine the position of companies in concentrated industries #13-15

6. Examine the effectiveness of shareholder control of a modern large corporation #16

7. Assess the importance of Crown corporations in Canada's economy #17-22

8. Review the key terms used in the chapter #23

Self-Test

1. State whether or not the story of Dan's Doughnut Dens illustrates each of the following:

   __T__(a) Sole proprietorship often involves a great deal of strain on the owner-manager.

   __T__(b) Partnerships are often subject to severe strains owing to differences among the partners.

   __T__(c) The corporate form of business enterprise can involve the risk of the original founder/owner/manager losing control of the business.

   __T__(d) Life insurance on the partners' lives is a common way to ensure the continuity of the business in the event of the death of one of the partners.

2. Name two advantages of the sole proprietorship as a form of business organization.

   (a) _freedom and flexability._

   (b) _easier to start_

3. List at least four disadvantages of the sole proprietorship as a form of business organization.

   (a) _full liability_
   tax burdens.

   (b) _employment_
   government problems.

17

(c) _____

_____

(d) _____

_____

4. In addition to the problems listed in the previous question, the partnership as a form of business organization faces the possible problem of

1. disagreement of opinions.

2. full liability issues.

5. List four advantages of the corporation as a form of business organization.

(a) limited liability.

(b) lower taxes

(c) easier to raise capital

(d) significant flexability.

6. The most common forms of small business ownership in Canada today are
 sole proprietorship and partnership.

7. State whether each of the following statements relates exclusively to a small business:

___Y__(a) A business qualifying for a lower tax rate of 25% on the first $250 000 of active income per year.

___Y__(b) A manufacturing business employing less than 100 employees.

___Y__(c) A non-manufacturing business with less than 50 employees.

___N__(d) A business with annual sales under $6 million.

___N__(e) A business having fewer than 100 shareholders.

8. Small business in Canada takes the form of:

 (a) sole proprietorships, partnerships and corporations.

 (b) sole proprietorships and partnerships only.

 (c) sole proprietorships only.

 (d) corporations only.

9. **TRUE** or **FALSE**:

 _T_ (a) From 1976 to 2002, the number of self-employed people in Canada grew by nearly 97%.

 _____ (b) Less than half of all new jobs in Canada are created by small business.

 _____ (c) Private corporations are required to publish extensive financial information to protect the investing public.

 _T_ (d) By 2002 women represented about 35% of all business owners in Canada.

 _____ (e) Small business can be found in the professions, service industry, agriculture, construction, and small-scale manufacturing.

10. Which of the following is not likely to be a small business?

 (a) a dental clinic with annual fees totalling $500 000.

 (b) a seafood restaurant.

 (c) a student enterprise.

 (d) a chain of nationally operated retail shoe outlets.

 (e) a turkey hatchery.

11. List four problems commonly faced by small businesses.

 (a) tax burdens

 (b) employment insurance

 (c) government problems

 (d) _____

12. The Canadian Federation of Independent Businesses (CFIB) is a small business lobby, raising issues concerning taxation, financing the purpose of which is to promote + protect of free competitive enterprises in Canada

13. Large businesses in Canada generally take the form of _public corporations_ because this form of business organization is most suited to the task of _raising_ _capital through stock + bonds._
    _____

14. Industrial corporate concentration is a concern to Canadians because
    _____
    _____

15. A multinational enterprise is one in which

    (a)   shareholders are spread throughout many different countries.

    (b)   resources are imported from one country to be processed in another.

    (c)   its business is conducted internationally in a number of different countries.

    (d)   shareholders are American and customers are Canadian.

16. Normally, the ultimate control of a corporation lies in the hands of _____
    _____

    However, when the shareholders are numerous and dispersed, control of large

    corporations is often exercised by _____

    or by _____.

    It should be noted that control is often separated from ownership. While 50%

    ownership in a corporation buys control in theory, often (more, less) is required in

    practice. Corporate executives or money managers can claim control and

    influence decisions based on their _____, rather than on

    ownership.

17. A Crown corporation is
    _____
    _____
    _____

18. State whether each of the following statements concerning Crown corporations in

    Canada is **TRUE** or **FALSE**.

    _____(a) They are few in number and therefore not a major part of the Canadian

             economy.

_____(b) Only the federal government has the power to create Crown
corporations.

_____(c) They are an important part of the Canadian economy, comprising
about 10% of Canada's very large corporations.

_____(d) Their objective is not merely to make a profit, but also in some cases
to provide certain services for the public.

19. List four types of industries in which Crown corporations have traditionally
played a significant role.

(a) _____

(b) _____

(c) _____

(d) _____

20. What is meant by "privatization"?

_____

_____

_____

21. In support of government enterprises, such as Canada Post and the Canadian
Broadcasting Corporation, it may be argued that _____

_____

_____

_____

_____

22. In opposition to the above argument, critics point out that _____

_____

_____

_____

_____

23.   Match the definitions on the right with the terms on the left.

B	Sole proprietorship	A	A business firm that is a separate legal entity from its owners, or shareholders, each of whose liability is limited to the amount of his or her investment in the firm.
E	Partnership	B	A business firm owned (and usually managed) by a single person who bears full legal liability for the firm's debts.
L	Limited partner	C	A public corporation has 50 or more shareholders.
F	General partners	D	The owners of shares (stocks) in a corporation.
A	Corporation	E	A business firm owned by two or more persons, with each person bearing full legal liability for the firm's debts.
D	Shareholders	F	Partners who take an active part in the management of the business and who have unlimited personal liability for its debts.
M	Boards of Directors	G	A private corporation has fewer than 50 shareholders.
G	Private corporation	H	Taxes paid by employers based on the number of their employees or the amount of payroll.
C	Public corporation	I	Businesses using processes and activities based on electronic information and data exchanges via the internet and the World Wide Web.
H	Payroll taxes	J	The process of selling government enterprises (usually Crown corporations) to private interests.
I	Ebusinesses	K	Corporations owned by a government and that are ultimately responsible, through a cabinet minister, to that government.
N	Proxies	L	A partner who invests in a business but takes no active part in the management of it, and whose liability is limited to the amount invested.
K	Crown corporations	M	A group of people elected by the shareholders of a corporation to provide direction to the management of the corporation.
J	Privatize	N	Legal instruments that allow a shareholder 's right to vote at shareholders' meetings to be delegated to another person, either with or without specific instructions as how to that vote will be exercised.

Micro Chapter 4

The Demand Side of Markets

This chapter explores the concept of consumer demand, focusing on major factors that affect demand. Demand is one of the most common terms used in economics, and as you work through this chapter you will realize that the concept of demand is much broader than you may have expected.

Essentially, when we speak of consumer demand for a particular product, we are referring to the entire schedule which relates the various quantities that a consumer would be willing to purchase of this product at different prices that might exist.

"Elasticity" of demand is also introduced in this chapter. This concept relates consumer sensitivity to price change in terms of the resulting changes in quantity purchased.

General Learning Objective

Develop an understanding of the concept of consumer demand.

Specific Learning Objectives

		Self-Test Reference
1.	Distinguish between the terms "demand" and "quantity demanded"	#1-6
2.	Outline the factors which influence consumer demand	#7-12
3.	Recognize factors affecting the elasticity of demand	#13-17
4.	Calculate the coefficient of the elasticity of demand	#18, 20-22
5.	Demonstrate the importance of demand elasticity as it relates to maximizing total revenue	#19, 23-29
6.	Review the key terms used in the chapter	#30

Micro Chapter 4

Self-Test

1.   Which one of the following portrays a typical demand curve?

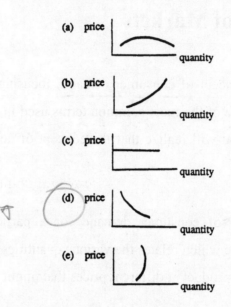

(a) price — quantity

(b) price — quantity

(c) price — quantity

(d) price — quantity

(e) price — quantity

2.   The demand curve in the previous question shows that as the price of a product rises, the quantity demanded _decreases_ .

3.   The change referred to in the above question is graphically illustrated by a curve that slopes _down_ .

4.   The term "quantity demanded" refers to_____

_____

_____

5.   Given the following data, plot the points and draw and label the curve.

Price	Quantity Demanded
$2	50
4	40
6	30
8	20
10	10

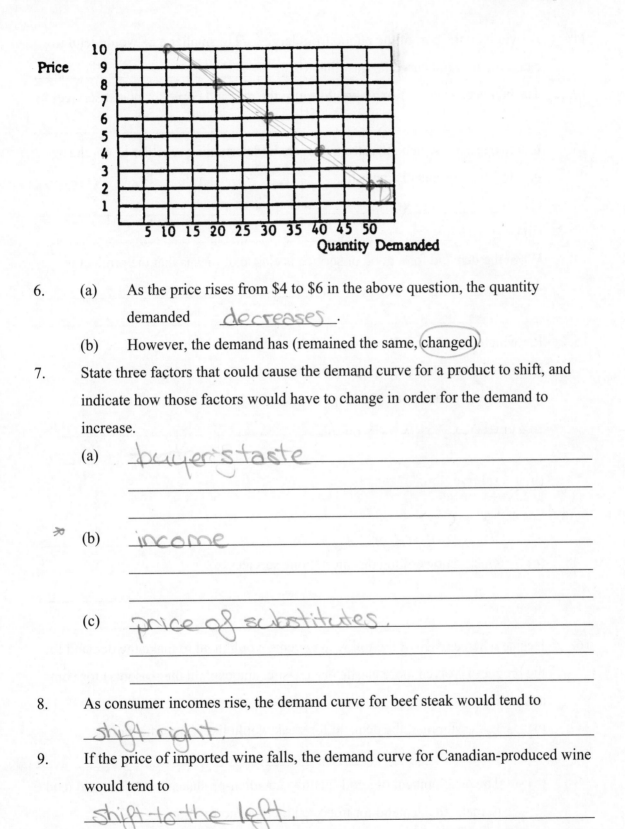

Price

Quantity Demanded

6. (a) As the price rises from $4 to $6 in the above question, the quantity
demanded _decreases_ .

(b) However, the demand has (remained the same, changed).

7. State three factors that could cause the demand curve for a product to shift, and
indicate how those factors would have to change in order for the demand to
increase.

(a) _buyer's taste_

(b) _income_

(c) _price of substitutes._

8. As consumer incomes rise, the demand curve for beef steak would tend to
shift right.

9. If the price of imported wine falls, the demand curve for Canadian-produced wine
would tend to
shift to the left.

10. If consumers in general began to prefer margarine to butter, the demand curve for
butter would tend to _shift to the left._

11. A switch on the part of the public from large cars to smaller cars would tend to cause the demand curve for gasoline to _Shift along the curve_

12. The increasing use of E-mail would cause the demand curve for postal services to _Shift to the left._

13. List two criteria which aid sales managers in determining whether or not the demand for a product is inelastic.

☆

(a) _no close substitutes._

(b) _the are unable to do w/o the product._

14. When the demand for a good or service is elastic, it means that the product is _price-sensative._

15. For which one of the following pairs of products would the demand be more elastic? Explain the reason(s) for your choices.

(a) automobiles/Ford Mustangs

Ford Mustangs

(b) salt/rye flour

rye flour.

(c) electric power/long distance phone services

electric power.

16. Decide whether each of the following events would tend to make the demand for the product involved more elastic or inelastic, and explain the reason(s) for your answers.

(a) In the summer, the demand for steak would likely become more _inelastic._

because _____

(b) The development of good-quality Canadian-produced melons would tend to make the demand for imported melons more _inelastic_,

because _____.

17. Consider the following products: (a) beef (b) meat (c) steak (d) porterhouse steak. Which of these do you think would be most elastic? _porterhouse_ Which would be least elastic? _meat_ Explain the reason for your answer. _____

_____ .

18.

Price	Quantity Demanded	Total Revenue
$5	100	$500
6	90	540
7	80	560
8	70	560
9	60	540

Indicate whether the demand represented in the above schedule is elastic, inelastic or of unitary elasticity for the following price changes:

(a) from $5 to $6: - inelastic

(b) from $6 to $7: - inelastic

(c) from $7 to $8: - unitary.

(d) from $8 to $9: - elastic

19. Based on the above question, if the firm lowered the price from $9 to $8, would the firm be better off or not? Explain your answer.

20. Elasticity may be expressed as the ratio of the percentage change in quantity to the percentage change in price:

coefficient of elasticity = percentage change in quantity
percentage change in price

or $\dfrac{\% \Delta Q}{\% \Delta P}$

You are the sales manager for a factory that produces bathroom faucets. Through an improvement in technology, the factory has been able to increase its production by 15%, and your objective is to sell the extra volume being produced. Past experience has shown that a 10% change in price will generate a 20% change in the quantity of faucets sold.

The elasticity coefficient is therefore _____, and demand is (elastic, inelastic, unit-elastic).

To generate a 15% increase in unit sales, price should be _____ by _____%.

If the average price of the product was initially $40, the new price will be $_____.

21.   If the coefficient of price elasticity of demand for a product is 10, it means that

(a)   a 10% change in price results in a 1% change in quantity demanded.

(b)   the product is insensitive to price changes.

(c)   a 1% change in price results in a 10% change in quantity demanded.

(d)   a change in price changes demand by an equal amount.

22.   Calculate the various elasticity coefficients for the demand curves below using the following formula:

$e =$ $\dfrac{Q2 - Q1}{(Q2 + Q1)/2}$: $\dfrac{P2 - P1}{(P2 + P1)/2}$ Where Q1 is the original quantity, P1 is the original price. Q2 and P2 are the new quantity and price.
e is used as the symbol for elasticity coefficient.

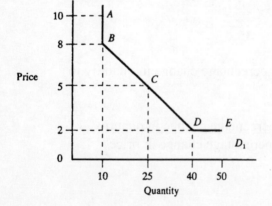

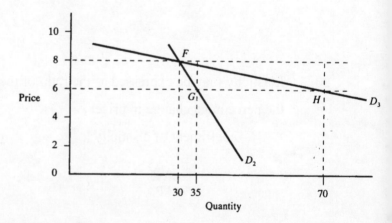

For　　A-B, e = _____.　　D-E, e = _____.

B-C, e = _____.　　F-G, e = _____.

C-D, e = _____.　　F-H, e = _____.

23.　　The (larger/smaller) the elasticity coefficient, the more sensitive a product is to price change.

24.　　If the legal minimum wage were to increase, then the total wage payments for industrial workers would fall if the demand for labour is (elastic/inelastic).

25.　　Complete the following table:

If Demand Is	Then *e* Is	If Price	Then Total Revenue Will
perfectly inelastic		decreases	
elastic		decreases	
		decreases	
inelastic	greater than 0 but less than 1	increases	
	infinitely large	remains constant	

26.　　If you were selling a product with an inelastic demand what would you emphasize, and not emphasize, in your advertising?

_____

_____

_____

_____

_____

27.　　If you were selling a product with an elastic demand what would you emphasize in your advertising?

_____

_____

_____

_____

_____

28. Brazilian coffee growers sometimes find it profitable to burn part of their crop. What effect would the burning of coffee by Brazilian coffee producers have if the demand for coffee were elastic?

_____

_____

_____

_____

_____

_____

29. One way in which workers attempt to raise their incomes is by joining a labour union. Would a union likely have more success at increasing the wages of plumbers or hairdressers? Explain the reasons for your answer.

_____

_____

_____

_____

_____

_____

30. Match the definitions on the right with the terms on the left.

	Demand	A	The percentage change in quantity demanded that results from a 1%-percent change in price.
	Elastic demand	B	The term used to describe demand if a price increase causes an increase in total sales revenue.
	Inelastic demand	C	The term used to describe demand if a price increase causes a reduction in total sales revenue.
	Coefficient of elasticity	D	The entire relationship between the various possible prices of a product or service and the quantity demanded at each price, expressed through either a schedule or a graph.

Micro Chapter 5

The Supply Side of Markets

This chapter presents the concepts of "supply" and how supply and demand interact in competitive markets to determine prices. One possible source of confusion is the terminology used to describe industries: the terms "competitive" and "concentrated" are intended to focus on industries' behaviour **regarding prices**, and to convey the idea that, in competitive industries, competition can be counted upon to hold down prices and profits, while in concentrated industries it cannot. This does not mean that there is a complete absence of competition among firms in concentrated industries: they often compete extensively through advertising, product improvement, or in attempting to increase their market share. However, there is a tendency for firms in such industries to seek to avoid competing on prices.

It is very important to remember that this chapter's analysis of supply deals only with competitive industries. In an equally important part of the economy, prices are determined differently, as will be seen later. Finally, static equilibrium analysis such as the supply/demand analysis of this chapter can be misleading. The equilibrium price is not "the" price; it is merely the result of the interaction between buyers and sellers in a market at a particular time. The behaviour of buyers and sellers (demand and supply) will constantly change, and so will the equilibrium price. It is helpful to think of the supply and demand curves as representing a snapshot of a changing situation at a particular point in time.

General Learning Objective

Examine the concept of producer supply and recognize the factors that influence supply.

Specific Learning Objectives

		Self-Test Reference
1.	Describe the conditions that distinguish competitive industries from concentrated industries	#1-6
2.	Distinguish between the terms "supply" and "quantity supplied"	#7, 8
3.	Outline the factors which cause changes in supply	#9-12
4.	Compare the conditions that cause supply to be elastic with those that cause an inelastic supply	#13-15
5.	Demonstrate a market equilibrium and indicate its significance with respect to price	#16-19
6.	Review the key terms used in the chapter	#20

Self-Test

1. Competitive industries are different from concentrated industries in that competitive industries

 (a) are those which compete for sales in international (export) markets.

 (b) are those in which there is any form of competition between firms (price, advertising, product differentiation, etc.).

 (c) are those in which there are many firms, which compete strongly on price.

 (d) include all industries which consist of more than one firm.

2. List the two basic characteristics of competitive industries.

 (a) _____

 (b) _____

3. As a result of the characteristics described in the previous question,

 (a) producers are unable to control either the supply of the product or its price, and profits tend to be low.

 (b) producers are able to control the supply of the product, forcing up its price and their profits.

 (c) producers can control the price of the product but not the supply of it.

(d)   producers can control prices, but are unable to keep out new firms and thus control supply.

(e)   product prices tend to be high because there are too many producers.

4.   List two ways in which the basic characteristics of concentrated industries differ from the basic characteristics of competitive industries as listed in (2) above.

(a)   _____

(b)   _____

5.   Because of the characteristics in (4) above, the behaviour of concentrated industries differs from the behaviour of competitive industries in that

_____

_____

6.   Indicate whether an economist would classify each of the following industries as competitive or concentrated

(a)   auto body repair shops _____

(b)   brewing _____

(c)   automobile manufacturing _____

(d)   restaurants _____

(e)   window washing _____

(f)   airlines _____

(g)   travel agencies _____

7.   Which of the graphs below represents the typical supply curve of a competitive industry?

8.   The supply curve reflects the fact that in competitive industries, as price increases,

_____

9.   (a)   If supply increases, the supply curve will _____

      (b)   Such an increase in supply could be caused by _____

10.   (a)   If supply decreases, the supply curve will _____

      (b)   Such a decrease in supply could be caused by _____

11.   As the costs of production rise in a given industry, the supply in that industry will

      _____. This is illustrated graphically by a shift _____ in the

      supply curve.

12.   As the number of firms in a given industry increases, the supply in that industry

      will _____. This is illustrated graphically by a shift

      _____ in the supply curve.

13.   (a)   If the supply of a product is inelastic, an increase in its price will

      _____

      (b)   What factors could make the supply of a product inelastic?

      _____

      _____

      _____

14.   (a)   If the supply of a product is elastic, an increase in its price will

      _____

      (b)   What could make the supply of a product elastic?

      _____

      _____

      _____

15.   As time passes, does the supply of most products become more elastic or more

      inelastic? Why?

      _____

16.

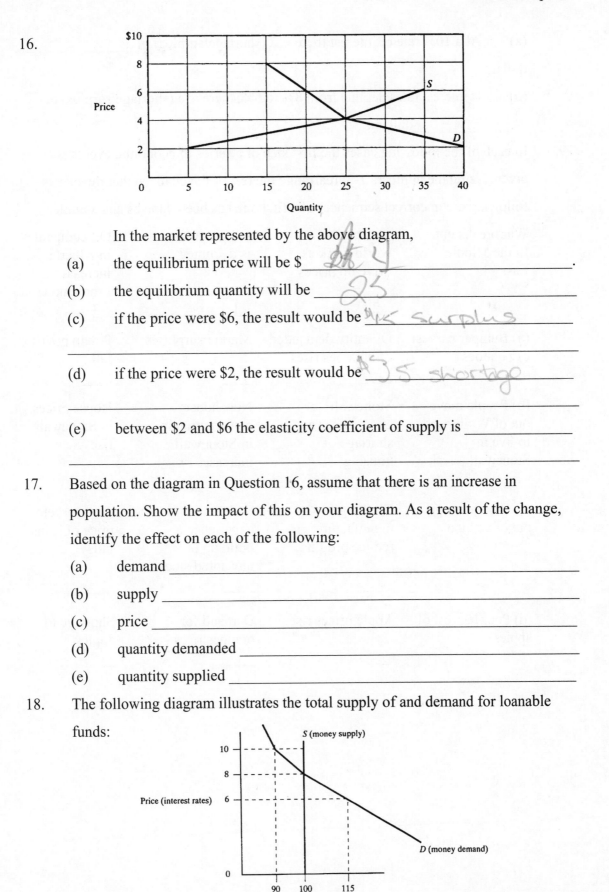

In the market represented by the above diagram,

(a)   the equilibrium price will be $ _____ 4 _____.

(b)   the equilibrium quantity will be _____ 25 _____

(c)   if the price were $6, the result would be _____ 15 surplus _____

_____

(d)   if the price were $2, the result would be _____ 35 shortage _____

_____

(e)   between $2 and $6 the elasticity coefficient of supply is _____

_____

17.   Based on the diagram in Question 16, assume that there is an increase in
       population. Show the impact of this on your diagram. As a result of the change,
       identify the effect on each of the following:

(a)   demand _____

(b)   supply _____

(c)   price _____

(d)   quantity demanded _____

(e)   quantity supplied _____

18.   The following diagram illustrates the total supply of and demand for loanable
       funds:

(a)   At a 10% rate of interest there is a (shortage/surplus) of _____
dollars

(b)   If interest rates decline from 8% to 6%, there is a (shortage/surplus) of
_____dollars.

19.   In each of the following cases the first step of a series of economic events is
given. Using the numbers 1-3, rearrange the rest of the chain so that the events
following are in correct sequence. The first one has been done as an example.

War breaks out In the Middle East	Shortage in world markets drive up prices	Oil production is disrupted	Oil companies in Alberta increase Production
	_2_	_1_	_3_
(a) Bumper harvest of potatoes	Quantity demanded of potatoes rises	Market surpluses	Potato prices fall
	_____	_____	_____
(b) People move out of Winnipeg to live in Stonewall	Stonewall experiences a shortage of housing	New house construction in in Stonewall increases	House prices in Stonewall rise
	_____	_____	_____
(c) Blue jeans go out of fashion	Clothing manufacturers reduce prod'n	Sellers experience a build up of unwanted stock	The market price of jeans falls
	_____	_____	_____
(d) Poor harvest of apples	Apple prices rise	Demand for oranges rises	Shortage of apples
	_____	_____	_____

20. Match the definitions on the right with the terms on the left.

	Market structure	A	The ability to raise one's prices; usually associated with a dominant or monopolistic position in the market.
	Competitive industry	B	Term used to describe the organization and nature of a market or an industry, particularly whether it is competitive or concentrated in nature.
	Market power	C	Term used to describe the position of the individual small firm in a competitive industry, which is unable to influence the price of its product and is forced to accept (take) whatever price is determined in the market.
	Concentrated industries	D	A graphical representation of a supply schedule.
	Price-maker	E	A situation in which quantity supplied does not increase readily when the price rises.
	Price-taker	F	A price determined in the market place by the interaction of supply and demand.
	Supply schedule	G	An industry that consists of many small firms and is easily entered by new competitors.
	Supply curve	H	The quantity sold (bought) at the equilibrium quantity
	Inelastic supply	I	Term used to describe the position of the dominant firm (s) in a concentrated industry, which can influence the price of the product.
	Elastic supply	J	A table depicting the relationship between the price of a product and the quantity supplied (offered for sale).
	Equilibrium price	K	A situation in which quantity supplied increases readily when the price rises.
	Equilibrium quantity	L	An industry that is dominated by a few large firms and is not easily entered by new competitors.

Micro Chapter 6

THE DYNAMICS OF COMPETITIVE MARKETS

This chapter uses the basic tools of supply and demand to show how competitive markets respond to changes in supply and demand. To illustrate the dynamics of competitive markets, various examples are used, including the markets for professional athletes and corporate presidents. The only new concept in this chapter is that the more elastic demand and supply are, the more smoothly a market will adjust to changes in supply or demand. It is important to remember that this type of supply-and-demand analysis relates only to the types of markets that we have classified as "competitive," that is, markets characterized by large numbers of sellers.

General Learning Objective

Demonstrate the dynamics of a competitive market under varying degrees of price elasticity and analyze the effects of government intervention in the market.

Specific Learning Objectives

		Self-Test Reference
1.	Illustrate the effect on market equilibrium of an increase/decrease in demand and supply	#1-4
2.	Establish the effect of demand elasticity on market equilibrium when supply shifts	#5
3.	Establish the effect of supply elasticity on market equilibrium when demand shifts	#6
4.	Compare the short run effect (supply inelastic) with the long run effect (supply more elastic) of a change in demand on market equilibrium	#7
5.	Observe the operation of demand and supply forces in other markets	#8-12

6.   Analyze the effect on the market of a government price support or control #13-17

7.   Review the key terms used in the chapter   #18

Self-Test

In answering Questions 1–4, you may find it helpful to draw the demand and supply curves.

1.   If the demand for the product increased (and the supply remained unchanged), the equilibrium price would _____ and the equilibrium quantity would

        _____.

2.   If the demand for the product decreased (and the supply remained unchanged), the equilibrium price would _____and the equilibrium quantity would

        _____.

3.   If the supply of the product increased (and the demand remained unchanged), the equilibrium price would _____ and the equilibrium quantity would

        _____.

4.   If the supply of the product decreased (and the demand remained unchanged), the equilibrium price would _____ and the equilibrium quantity would

        _____.

5.   An increase in demand for a product will result in a greater increase in price,

        (a)   the more inelastic is the supply of the product.

        (b)   the more elastic is the supply of the product.

        (c)   the larger is the supply of the product.

        (d)   the smaller is the supply of the product.

        (e)   none of the above.

6.   A decrease in the supply of a product will result in a greater increase in price,

        (a)   the more elastic is the demand for the product.

        (b)   the more inelastic is the demand for the product.

        (c)   the larger is the demand for the product.

        (d)   the smaller is the demand for the product.

        (e)   none of the above.

7.   As time progresses, the supply of products tends to become

        (a)   less elastic.

        (b)   more elastic.

        (c)   neither more nor less elastic.

8.   Salaries for professional athletes have greatly increased in recent years, even
        though the quality of athlete has not increased. This could be best explained by:

        (a)   A decrease in supply of professional athletes.

        (b)   A decrease in demand for professional athletes.

        (c)   An increase in supply of professional athletes.

        (d)   An increase in demand for professional athletes.

9.   The president of a large company and an assembly line worker may work equally
        hard at their jobs, but the president of the company receives much more income.
        Explain why in terms of demand and supply.

        _____

        _____

10.   The following diagram refers to the market for cauliflower.

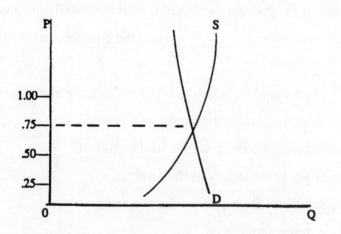

        Producers currently are selling cauliflower at a price of $1.00 each. Can this price
        prevail in this market? Why or why not?

        _____

        _____

        _____

        _____

11.   Improved technology generally is welcomed as a positive factor for the producer
        and the economy in general. In the case of grain farmers, there have been
        significant improvements in production methods over the past twenty years due to
        technological innovation, but a reduction in income for grain farmers. Why has
        this happened? Explain how technology has affected supply and/or demand of
        grain.

        _____

        _____

        _____

        _____

        _____

        _____

        _____

12.   The following diagram illustrates the market for residential real estate in Halifax
        as of May 2000.

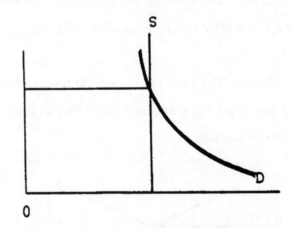

        For each of the following factors, determine the effect on the housing market (i.e.,
        demand, supply, equilibrium price, equilibrium quantity)

        (a)   There is a substantial decrease in residential mortgage rates.

        (b)   Contractors realize improved profit margins for residential housing
                construction relative to other buildings.

        (c)   A recession occurs with increasing unemployment and a fear of future job
                losses.

Answer Questions 13-15 on the basis of the following graph.

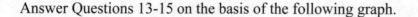

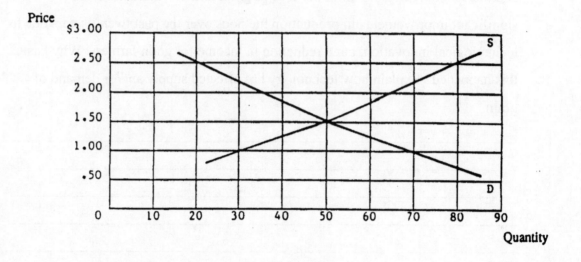

13.   The equilibrium price of this product will be $ _____ per unit.

14.   If the government supported the price of this product above the equilibrium price,
       at a price of $2.50, the result would be_____

       _____

15.   If the government placed controls on the price of this product to hold it below the
       equilibrium price, at a price of $1, the result would be _____

       _____

16.   The following diagram illustrates the market for rental accommodation in Red
       Lake for 2-bedroom walk-up apartments. Equilibrium price is P1 and equilibrium
       quantity is Q1 in the market.

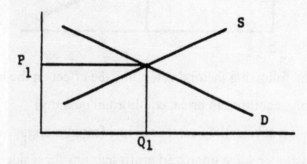

       Now suppose that there is an enormous increase in the town's population due to a
       mining boom resulting from the opening of three new gold mines in the area.

Assume that the Mayor wishes to maintain rent levels at P1 and therefore initiates rent controls to do so.

(a)   What will be the effect of the increase in population on the equilibrium price and quantity for rental accommodation?

_____

_____

(b)   What will be the long-term implications if price controls maintain rental prices at the old equilibrium price?

_____

_____

(c)   Illustrate using the above diagram.

_____

_____

17.   If the minimum wage were $6.00/hour and the labour market were in equilibrium at that wage rate, what would be the effect of an increase in the minimum wage to $7.00/hour?

_____

_____

18.   Match the definitions on the right with the terms on the left.

	Price support (floor)	A	A legal limit on a price or on increases in a price, which holds the price below its equilibrium level.
	Price control (ceiling)	B	Legal limits on the level or rents and /or on the rents increases charged by landlords.
	Rent controls	C	The situation when quantity demanded is less than quantity supplied.
	Shortage	D	An artificially high price, held above the equilibrium level by the government.
	Surplus	E	The situation when quantity supplied is less than quantity demanded.

Micro Chapter 7

Market Structures

This chapter examines the operation of competitive and concentrated industries. Competitive industries are divided into two types: perfect competition and monopolistic competition. Perfect competition is a rather abstract and theoretical concept, but it does provide a useful starting point, or benchmark, for comparing the performances of other types of industries, since it represents the most extremely competitive situation possible — one in which each seller has absolutely no control over the price of its product.

Monopolistic competition represents a much more realistic and relevant type of industry. Unfortunately, monopolistic competition is a label which many students find confusing, as the term "monopolistic" leads them to think of Bell Canada rather than Harry's Hamburger Stand. It is essential to remember that monopolistically competitive industries are also highly competitive, and that the product differentiation which characterizes these industries only gives some sellers a small degree of control over the price of their products.

Concentrated industries are also divided into two types: oligopoly and monopoly. Oligopoly is a very large and important sector of the Canadian economy characterized by a few producers dominating the market. However, predicting the behaviour of oligopolists regarding price and output decision is not simple. The potential for increasing prices and profits above competitive levels exists with the actual result depending on the particular circumstance.

The section on monopoly describes an industry with only one producer. This situation is unique as this one supplier has complete control over the total amount produced and the price charged. This is a relatively small sector of the Canadian economy mostly limited to government owned monopolies.

General Learning Objective

Distinguish between perfect competition, monopolistic competition, oligopoly and monopoly. Examine the effect on market prices and output.

Specific Learning Objectives

		Self-Test Reference
1.	Identify the conditions necessary for perfect competition	#1
2.	Diagram the theory of market prices determination under perfect competition	#2-4
3.	Identify the characteristics of monopolistic competition	#5, 6
4.	Compare the demand curve facing a monopolistically competitive firm with that of a perfect competitor	#7-9
5.	Identify the reasons for the relatively low prices and profits of competitive industries	#10
6.	Identify the characteristics of oligopoly	#11-13
7.	Examine barriers to entry	#14, 15
8.	Analyze price determination in an oligopolistic structure	#16, 17
9.	Inspect forms of non-price rivalry practised by oligopolists	#18, 19
10.	Define a monopoly industry	#20-22
11.	Determine the factors that affect market power	#23
12.	Classify Canadian industries	#24
13.	Review the key terms used in the chapter	#25

Self-Test

1. Name the three characteristics of perfect competition.

    (a) _many small firms_

    (b) _easy to entre_

    (c) _goods/services are identical_

2. If an individual seller under perfect competition raises the price of its product, its sales will _decrease_.

3. (a) On the graph, draw the demand curve for the product of an individual firm in a perfectly competitive industry in which the market price is $4.

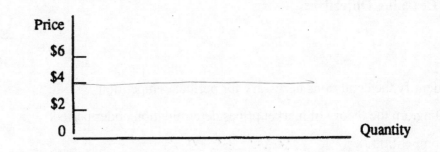

Price
$6
$4
$2
0   Quantity

(b) What is the price charged and the quantity sold of the above firm?

Price charged = $4

(c) What can the firm do to increase its profits above minimal levels?

increase efficiency by lowering per unit production cost.

4. Frank Smith is one of thousands of grain farmers who produces only #1 Northern wheat. Last year he harvested and sold 320 000 bushels. The market price was $3.80 per bushel and the total Canadian production was 2 billion bushels. Assume no government intervention.

(a) Choose the best description of the industry.

   (i)   monopoly   (iii) oligopoly
   (ii) monopolistic competition   (iv)   perfect competition

(b) Why did you make the choice in part (a)?

each farmer has the same product.

(c) Draw the demand schedule facing Mr. Smith.

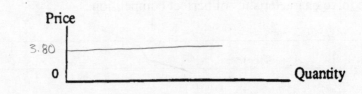

Price
3.80
0   Quantity

(d)   What happens if Smith increases his price slightly above the market price?

his profits would decrease.

(e)   Should Smith lower his price below $3.80 to capture more of the wheat

market? Why or why not? _reducing price_

reduces profits.

(f)   Should Smith spend money on advertising?

no, this would wald reduce profits

5.   State two characteristics of perfect competition and monopolistic competition

which are similar.

(a)   _many small firms_

(b)   _easy to entre_

6.   Monopolistic competition is different from perfect competition in that, in

monopolistic competition, _goods or services_

are differentiated from one another.

7.   In monopolistic competition:

(a)   each seller has a great deal of control over the price of its product.

(b)   producers usually make agreements not to compete on prices.

(c)   the demand for each seller's product is more elastic than in perfect

competition.

(d)   while profits are still quite low, individual sellers have a small degree of

control over the prices of their products.

(e)   the one seller has total control of the market.

8.   As product differentiation increases, demand tends to

(a)   rise.

(b)   fall.

(c)   become more elastic.

(d)   become neither more nor less elastic.

(e)   become more inelastic.

9.   Bob Van Heyden owns a bakery in a city where there are over one hundred other bakeries. Bob specializes in Belgian pastries and is known for his fine birthday cakes. Last year he lowered his prices for one month only to find that total sales revenues declined from $16 000 to $13 500.

   (a)   Choose the best description of the industry.

      (i)   monopoly   (iii)   monopolistic competition

      (ii)   oligopoly   (iv)   perfect competition

   (b)   Demand for Bob's bakery products around the market price appears to be (inelastic/elastic).

   (c)   What accounts for the nature of the elasticity of (b)?

   the total profit decline

   (d)   What is Bob's most important advantage in capturing and holding his market relative to his competitors? _Belgian pastries & B-day cakes._

10.   Competitive industries are characterized by low prices and low profits. The origin of this situation is best described by

   (a)   aggressive price cutting.

   (b)   extraordinary advertising expenditures.

   (c)   a large number of firms.

   (d)   easy entry into the industry.

   (e)   an inability of producers to control supply.

   (f)   Choices (c), (d), and (e).

11.   Oligopoly refers to a situation in which

   (a)   an industry is dominated by a few large firms.

   (b)   prices and profits are above competitive levels.

   (c)   two or three firms do all of the business in a particular market.

   (d)   one very large corporation is the largest (but not the only) firm in a particular market.

   (e)   none of the above.

12. "Oligopoly" is defined as a situation in which ___4___ or fewer producers account for ___50___ % or more of an industry's sales.

13. Regal Steel Ltd. is a privately owned steel manufacturer competing in an industry where three firms have a near equal share of the market. Each firm specializes in a unique steel product ranging from steel for automobiles to the rolled steel of pipelines. Regal sells its product for $1500 per tonne and sold 2 million tonnes last year. The owners feel that a 10% price increase will cause a reduction in sales to 1.6 million tonnes. It also seems apparent that a 10% price reduction will increase sales to 2.1 million tonnes.

    (a) This is an example of

        (i) monopoly   (iii) monopolistic competition

        (ii) oligopoly   (iv) perfect competition

    (b) Three reasons for choosing the answer in (a) are _____

    _____

    _____

    _____

    (c) Should Regal increase the price of the product by 10%? Why or why not?

    no because there would be a
    reduction in sales.

    _____

    (d) Should Regal decrease its price by 10%? Why or why not?

    no because his profits would be lower.

(e)   Draw the demand schedule facing the Regal Steel Co. in the following space.

Price
($ per tonne)

Quantity (tonnes per year)

(f)   Above $1500 demand is (inelastic/elastic) whereas below $1500 demand is (inelastic/elastic).

14.   List six different types of barriers to entry which may make it difficult for new firms to enter an industry.

(a)   _____

(b)   _____

(c)   _____

(d)   _____

(e)   _____

(f)   _____

15.   State whether it is TRUE or FALSE that barriers to entry to an industry tend to have each of the following effects

_____ (a)   To increase competition and reduce prices and profits.

_____ (b)   To restrict competition and increase prices and profits.

_____ (c)   To make existing producers more efficient, thus reducing product prices.

_____ (d)   To increase production by existing producers in the industry.

16.   The demand curve faced by an oligopolist creates an incentive for the oligopolist
       to

       (a)   increase its price.

       (b)   leave its price at the present level.

       (c)   change its price only if the other firms in the industry do so.

       (d)   (b) and (c) are both correct.

       (e)   reduce its price.

17.   If oligopolists are to succeed in controlling the price of their product, they must
       succeed in controlling the _____ of it.

18.   State whether each of the following types of competition would likely be used by
       oligopolists.

       _____ (a)   advertising

       _____ (b)   customer services

       _____ (c)   product differentiation

       _____ (d)   price reductions

       _____ (e)   style changes

19.   During a recession, competitive industries tend to adjust to reduced demand by
       _____, while oligopolistic industries tend to adjust to reduced demand by

       _____

20.   The best definition of a monopoly industry is _____

       _____

21.   The secret of the De Beers monopoly of the diamond market could be attributed
       to

       (a)   influencing demand through the advertising campaign of "A diamond is
              forever."

       (b)   limiting production and the number of dealers.

       (c)   forcing Russian diamonds off the market through negative advertising.

       (d)   a policy of selling diamonds at the wholesale level.

       (e)   both (a) and (b).

22.   Compared to competitive industries, a monopoly will tend to produce

    (a)   a higher output at a higher price.

    (b)   the same output at a higher price.

    (c)   a lower output at a higher price.

    (d)   none of the above.

23.   State whether each of the following will increase or decrease the market power of firms within an industry.

    (a)   merger of several producers

    (b)   elimination of tariffs

    (c)   better substitutes become available

    (d)   reduction in patent lengths

    (e)   increase in licensing fees

    (f)   higher capital requirements

    (g)   formation of a cartel

24.   Classify each of the following types of industries in Canada as perfect competition, monopolistic competition, oligopoly, or monopoly.

    (a)   telephone — local service

    (b)   telephone — long distance service

    (c)   breweries

    (d)   hydroelectric

    (e)   restaurants

    (f)   service stations

    (g)   postal service

    (h)   vegetable farmers

    (i)   steel mills

    (j)   record stores

25. Match the definitions on the right with the terms on the left.

	Perfect competition	A	A situation in which four or fewer firms account for at least half of the sales of an industry.
	Perfectly elastic demand	B	A term used to describe prices that have been fixed by sellers.
	Monopolistic competition	C	A situation in which there is only one seller of a particular good or service.
	Product differentiation	D	A term describing industries that consists of a large number of small firms, where entry to the industry by new firms is easy, and where all firms in the industry sell identical products.
	Oligopoly	E	A situation in which any price increase above the market price will cause a firm's sales to fall to zero; represented by a horizontal demand curve.
	Monopoly	F	A term describing industries that consists of a large number of small firms, where entry to the industry by new firms is easy, and where all firms in the industry sell identical products.
	Price-fixing	G	Attempts by individual firms to distinguish their products or services from those of their competitors.
	Administered prices	H	A technique of price-fixing in which one firm (the price leader) sets its price and the rest in the industry follow suit.
	Price leadership	I	Agreements among oligopolists to raise their prices above levels that would prevail in a competitive situation.
	Cartel	J	Competition between sellers based not on price but rather on factors such as product differentiation and advertising.
	Non-price competition	K	An industry, such as public utilities, that by its nature lends itself to a monopolistic form of organization.
	Natural monopoly	L	A formal agreement among producers to coordinate their prices and output decisions for the purpose of earning monopoly profits.

Micro Chapter 8

The Costs and Revenues of the Firm

Chapter 7 covered the four types of Market Structures (perfect competition, monopolistic competition, oligopoly and monopoly) and the behaviour of these industries regarding price and output decisions. In explaining the incentives facing the individual firm regarding its price and output decisions, we have so far assumed that the firm's objective was to maximize its total revenue (sales revenue), rather than profits. This made the analysis simpler, as it enabled us to focus on the revenues of the business, whereas analyzing profits would have required consideration of production costs as well as sales revenues.

Chapter 8 adds the topic of production costs to make that analysis more complete. This requires the introduction of some new concepts (in particular, the Law of Diminishing Returns and its effect on costs, and the concepts of marginal cost and marginal revenue and the analysis associated with them). These new concepts can only be learned effectively by working with them and by doing the problems in the discussion questions and the self-test questions.

When these new tools of analysis are used, our understanding of the behaviour of the individual firm under various market structures is more thorough. However, the results of the analysis — our conclusions regarding the incentives facing the firm regarding its price and output decisions under various market structures — are the same.

General Learning Objectives

Using production cost data and sales revenue projections, determine the maximum profit output under conditions of both perfect and imperfect competition.

Specific Learning Objectives

1.	Distinguish between fixed and variable costs	#1-2
2.	Relate average variable costs to average product per worker	#3-5
3.	Understand average costs of a typical firm	#6
4.	Calculate marginal costs from marginal productivity data	#7-9
5.	Consider average and marginal costs of a typical firm	#10, 11
6.	Relate productivity data to the firm's costs, revenues and profits	#12
7.	Determine the maximum profit output for a perfectly competitive firm	#13, 14
8.	Illustrate a monopolist's maximum profit price and output position	#15,16
9.	Analyze the break-even position and the shut-down point for a business firm	#17,18
10.	Review the key terms used in the chapter	#19

Note: When constructing graphs, plot the marginal cost and marginal revenue data at the midpoint of the appropriate range of output. For example, if marginal cost is $10 between 100 and 200 units, plot the $10 at 150 units.

Self-Test

1. State whether each of the following is a fixed or variable cost.

        _____ (a)   property taxes

        _____ (b)   flat-rate telephone costs

        _____ (c)   direct materials costs

        _____ (d)   direct labour costs

        _____ (e)   the salary of the president

        _____ (f)   mortgage payments

        _____ (g)   long-distance telephone services

2.   As output increases, fixed costs per unit

    (a)   increase.

    (b)   remain constant.

    (c)   decrease.

3.   As successive units of one production input (e.g., labour) are added to fixed amounts of other inputs (e.g., capital equipment), the average output of the variable input will

    (a)   increase at a constant rate.

    (b)   remain unchanged.

    (c)   increase at first, then decline.

    (d)   decrease gradually.

    (e)   none of the above.

4.   The phenomenon described in Question 3 is known as the

_____

_____

5.   As output is increased, average variable cost per unit

    (a)   falls at first, then rises.

    (b)   rises at first, then falls.

    (c)   falls continually.

    (d)   rises continually.

    (e)   none of the above.

6.   Average total cost per unit is a dish-shaped curve.

    (a)   It is high at low levels of output because

_____

_____

    (b)   It is high at high levels of output because

_____

_____

7.	Marginal cost per unit is

(a)	the addition to total costs arising from the production of one more unit.

(b)	the total costs divided by the total number of units produced.

(c)	the total variable costs divided by the number of units produced.

(d)	the net effect of declining fixed costs per unit and rising variable costs per unit as output is increased.

(e)	none of the above.

8.	If output is increased from 25 units to 26 units and total costs increase from $615 to $638, marginal cost per unit is

(a)	$24.60.

(b)	$24.54.

(c)	$23.

(d)	$638.

(e)	none of the above.

9.	Fill in the "marginal cost per unit" column

Output	Total Costs	Marginal Cost per Unit
0	$200	æ
5	300	$_____ (a)
10	385	$_____ (b)
15	460	$_____ (c)

10.	If average cost per unit is falling,

(a)	marginal cost per unit must be falling faster than average cost per unit.

(b)	marginal cost per unit must be rising.

(c)	marginal cost per unit must be less than average cost per unit.

(d)	marginal cost per unit must be falling, too.

(e)	none of the above.

11.	The marginal cost per unit curve intersects the average cost per unit curve

(a)	to the left of the lowest point on the average cost per unit curve.

(b)	at the lowest point on the average cost per unit curve.

(c)	to the right of the lowest point on the average cost per unit curve.

12. Joe Smith has a business manufacturing television tables. His building is 2000 square feet and his fixed costs are $600 per week.

Each employee hired costs the company $1500 per week.

The owner discovered the following changes to weekly output as more labour was hired. Determine average output for the various levels of employment.

Labour per week (employees)	Output per Week Week	Average Output (tables/employee)
1	20	
2	40	
3	90	
4	150	
5	160	

(a) Peak efficiency for this business seems to occur at _____ tables per week and _____ employees.

(b) The law of diminishing returns is illustrated when the _____ employee is hired.

(c) The costs incurred when hiring employees is usually known as

_____.

(d) Complete the following table by determining costs at each output level.

(1) Employees	(2) Tables	(3) Total Fixed Costs (FTC)	(4) Total Variable Costs (VTC)	(5) Total Costs	(6) ATC
0	0				
1	20				
2	40				
3	90				
4	150				
5	160				

(e)   Suppose the selling price for each table is $55.00 and the firm can sell all that it produces. Complete the following.

Tables/Week	Total Revenue	Total Costs	Profits
20	$		
40	$		
90	$		
150	$		
160	$		

(f)   Thus, for this business, the best level of production is _____ tables per week. The firm hires _____ employees and total profits are $ _____ per week.

(g)   Under what conditions would this firm decide to shut down rather than continuing to operate in the short-run period?

13.   The Rory Street Bike Works is a small bicycle manufacturing company. Presently, there are two employees who are manufacturing 3 bicycles per day. The owners wish to know whether to expand their operation and if so by how much. After completing part (a), make their decision in (b) given the following data.

Each worker is paid $60 per day.

Total fixed costs are $50 per day.

There are $20 of materials in each bicycle.

Each bicycle sells for $75.

(a)   Fill in the blanks on the following tables and complete the graphs. Plot total revenues and total costs on one graph and marginal cost and marginal revenue on the other.

Labour	Daily Output	Fixed Costs	Total Variable Costs	Total Cost	Average Total Cost	Marginal Cost	Total Revenues	Profits	Marginal Revenues
0	0								
1	1								
2	3								
3	7								
4	9								
5	10								

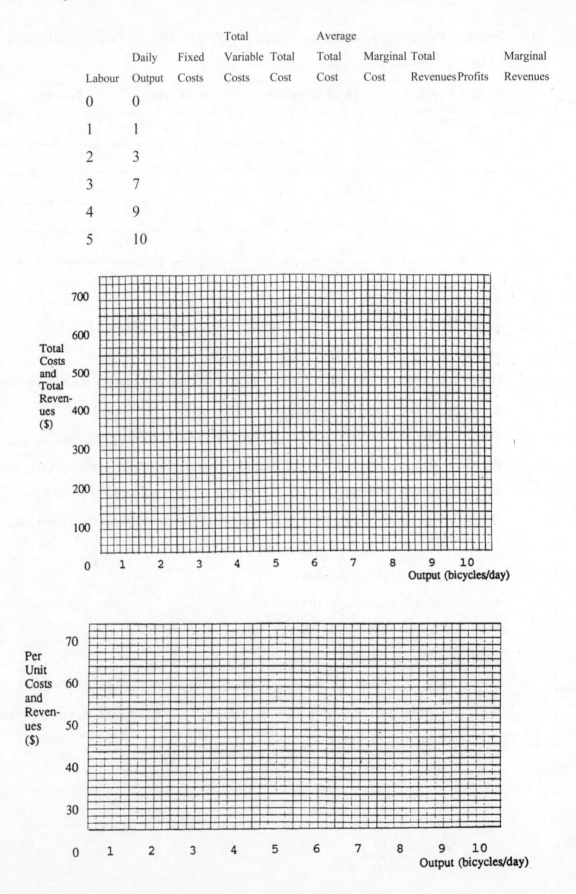

(b)   Decision: Employees _____

        Output _____

        Profits _____

(c)   Assuming production and sales occur according to your recommendation, why
        wouldn't this firm hire one more person (i.e., five in total) and produce and sell
        one more bicycle (i.e., ten in total)?

        _____

        _____

(d)   Suppose the market price for their product falls to $40 per bicycle. What is the
        best decision for the owners assuming these costs are unchanged? Why?

        _____

        _____

14.

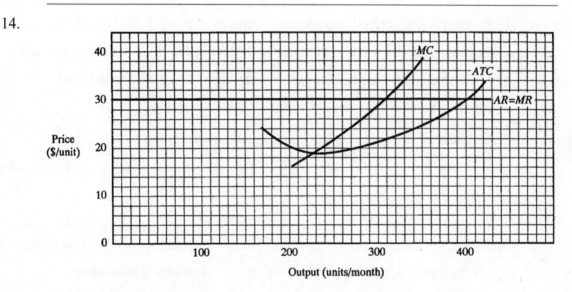

For the firm whose costs and revenues are shown in the above graph,

(a)   profits will be maximized at a level of output of

        _____

        units, and

(b)   at this level of output, profits will be $_____.

Show your calculations assuming that ATC = $22 at the best level of output.

(Work through both methods.)

Micro Chapter 8

Method 1:   Method 2:

Profit/Unit: Price – ATC   Total Revenues: Best Output x Price

_____ – _____ = _____   _____ x _____

Total Profits: Total Costs:

Profits/Unit x Best Output   Best Output x ATC

= $_____ x _____   _____ x _____

= $_____   = $_____

                                           Total Profits: TR – TC

                                           = _____

(c)   Is this firm operating in a perfectly competitive market?

       YES _____

       NO _____

If this firm is in a perfectly competitive industry and is a typical firm which is making extra profits, what adjustment will occur in the price of the product and how will this affect the profits of this typical firm? What will be the final equilibrium level of the price?

_____

_____

_____

_____

15.   Following are the cost and revenue data for the Ronson Reemistram Company.

If the company charges this price per reemistram:	It will sell this many reemistrams per week:
$ 5.00	0
4.50	300
4.00	600
3.50	900
3.00	1200
2.50	1500
2.00	1800

The company's total fixed costs (TFC) are $300 per week, and its total variable costs (TVC) are shown in the following table.

Daily Output	$ TFC	$ TVC	$ Total Costs	ATC	(AR) Average Revenue or Price	(TR) Total Revenue	(MC) Marginal Cost	(MR) Marginal Revenue
0	300	0						
300		850						
600		1550						
900		2050						
1200		2500						
1500		3100						
1800		4300						

(a)   Determine the values for the blanks in the above table.

(b)   Draw the ATC, MC, AR and MR schedules on the graph. (Remember to plot MC and _____ MR at the midpoints of the range.)

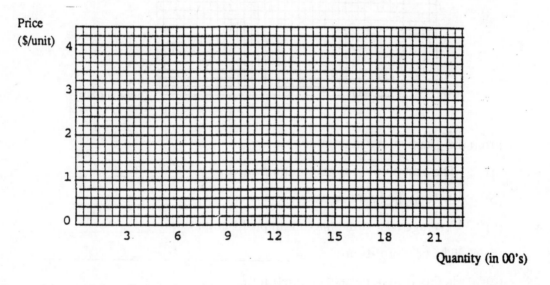

(c)   According to the table, the best level of output for the maximum profits is in the range of _____ units.

(d)   According to the graph, the best profit point occurs at _____ units.

(e)   If ATC = $2.40 and price is $3.25 at the best output, total daily profits are
$_____

(f)   Is the Ronson Company operating in a perfectly competitive market?
Yes _____   No _____
How do you know in this situation?

16.

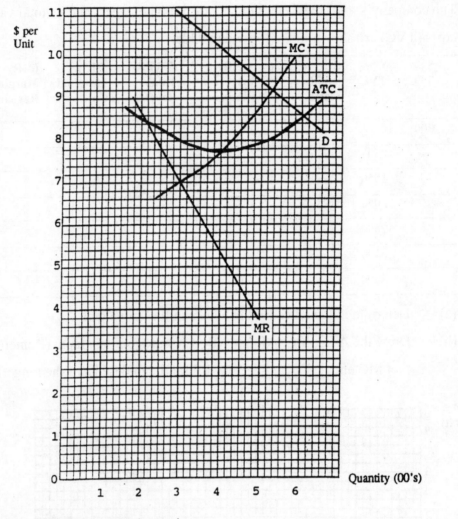

From the graph above determine:

(a)   The best output for maximum profits _____

(b)   Price at the best output _____

(c)   Average cost at the maximum profit output _____

(d)   The best profits are _____

(e)   Is this firm in perfect competition? _____

Reason: _____

_____

_____

_____

_____

17.   Given the following data:

Quantity	Price	Total Costs	Total Revenues
0	$50	100	_____
10	$50	500	_____
20	$50	950	_____
30	$50	1400	_____
40	$50	1600	_____
50	$50	3000	_____

(a)   Fill in the table for total revenues.

(b)   Draw the graph of total revenues and total costs using the grid on the following page.

(c)   Determine the best output to maximize profits. Show this point on the graph by drawing a vertical line up to TC and TR.

(d)   What is the break-even level of output according to the table?

_____. Show the two points of break-even on the graph.

(e)   What is the level of total fixed costs? _____

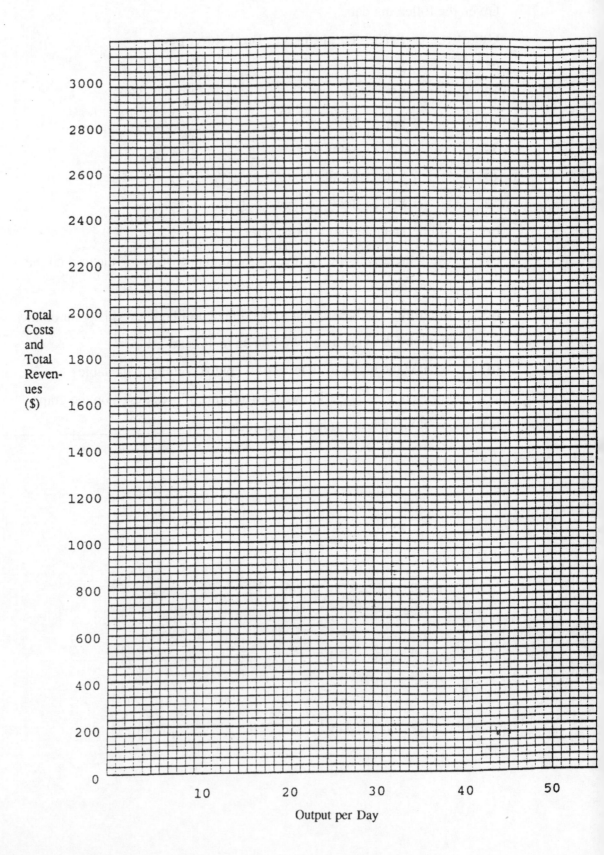

18.   Francesca's Fradistats Ltd. sells fradistats at a price of $3.50 each. Francesca's fixed variable costs are shown in the following table.

Units of Output per Day	Fixed Costs	Variable Costs	Total Costs	Total Revenue
0	$300	$0	_____	_____
200	300	900	_____	_____
400	300	1600	_____	_____
600	300	2100	_____	_____
800	300	2400	_____	_____
1000	300	3100	_____	_____
1200	300	4300	_____	_____

(a)   Complete the remaining 2 columns in the table.

(b)   On the graph below, draw the total revenue, total costs and variable costs curves.

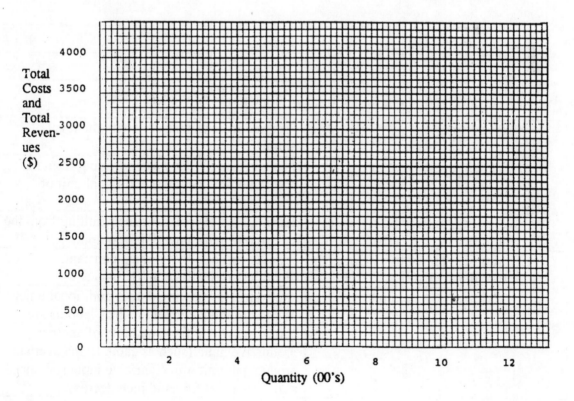

(c)   The graph indicates that the minimum level of output and sales required for this firm to start up in business (its break-even point) is _____ units per day.

(d)   The graph indicates that, before this firm should go out of business, its sales should fall below a level of _____ units per day.

Explain the reasons for your answers to (c) and (d).

_____

_____

_____

_____

_____

_____

_____

_____

_____

_____

_____

19.   Match the definitions on the right with the terms on the left.

	Fixed costs	A	Production costs that vary with the level of output.
	Variable costs	B	The addition to total costs resulting from the production of one more additional unit of output.
	Law of Diminishing Returns	C	The addition to total revenue resulting from the sale of one additional unit of output.
	Marginal productivity (per worker)	D	Production costs that remain constant, regardless of the level of output.
	Marginal cost per unit	E	A physical law stating that, if additional units of one productive input (such as labour) are combined with a fixed quantity of another productive input (such as capital), the average product per unit of the variable input (labour) will increase at first and then decrease.
	Marginal revenue per unit	F	The increase in production resulting from the hiring of one additional worker.

Micro Chapter 9

Government Policy Toward Business

This chapter deals with issues of big business and government policy in Canada. This is an important policy issue due to the small size of much of the Canadian manufacturing sector's operations and its vulnerability to foreign competition.

Chapter 9 examines the traditional view that "big is bad." It is difficult to estimate the effect that oligopolistic practices have on prices, and the estimate that oligopoly results in prices being 25% higher than would exist under competitive conditions is based on a limited amount of research; however, it is the best estimate available.

Subsequently, it is argued that the traditional view is not correct, for various reasons. The key element in this argument is that the price comparisons presented may not always be appropriate because the lower production costs associated with the larger operations of big businesses make it possible for prices to be reasonable despite their higher profits. Thus, it is argued, big business actually contributes to our prosperity through its productivity by increasing capital investment.

The policy dilemma which flows from these differences of opinion is discussed, stressing its relevance to the importance of improving the international competitive position of the Canadian manufacturing sector. While Canadian industry is more concentrated than industry in other countries, Canadian firms are small by international standards and not particularly competitive internationally. So, if revisions to Canadian competition policy result in increasing the restrictions on the growth of big business in order to give consumers more protection, they risk preventing Canadian firms from becoming larger and more competitive internationally. Recent changes to Canadian competition policy appear to be geared to legal considerations, such as anti-competitive behaviour, as opposed to economic considerations, such as the desirability of larger, more efficient Canadian manufacturing enterprises.

General Learning Objective

Discuss whether or not industrial concentration is in the best interests of the Canadian economy.

Specific Learning Objectives

		Self-Test Reference
1.	Give reasons for and examples of increased industrial concentration in Canada's manufacturing sector	#1-4
2.	Describe the probable costs of increased industrial concentration to Canada	#5-10
3.	Describe the probable benefits of increased industrial concentration to Canada	#11-15
4.	Discuss the policy dilemma facing the Canadian government regarding industrial concentration	#16-26
5.	Identify major changes in emphasis in the new competition policy in Canada	#27-28
6.	Review the key words used in the chapter	#29

Self-Test

1. List a few reasons for mergers of Canadian companies in 1990s.

    (a) _____

    (b) _____

    (c) _____

2.   Industrial concentration refers to

    (a)   situations in which one firm controls over half of the sales of an industry.

    (b)   the extent to which an industry is dominated by a few firms.

    (c)   only those industries in which profits are significantly above the average for the economy as a whole.

    (d)   industries in which the major firm(s) concentrate(s) on acquiring the shares of their competitors.

    (e)   none of the above.

3.   Industrial concentration is of interest and concern to economists because

    (a)   larger firms are sometimes more progressive technologically, and thus contribute to higher productivity and higher living standards.

    (b)   when a few firms dominate an industry, the potential exists for monopolistic practices such as price-fixing.

    (c)   it is generally agreed that big business and the domination of industries by a few firms are economically and socially undesirable.

    (d)   (b) and (c) together.

    (e)   (a) and (b) together.

4.   In Canada, the overall degree of industrial concentration is higher than in the USA. **TRUE** or **FALSE?**

5.   State whether each of the following is a reason why large corporations have come to play such a dominant role in much of the economy.

    _____ (a)   Larger businesses often enjoy cost advantages, due to large-scale production, and are thus better able to compete.

    _____ (b)   Modern manufacturing often requires such vast amounts of capital investment and large plants that large corporations are required.

    _____ (c)   Government prefers large corporations to smaller businesses, and it is government policy to encourage the development of large corporations, through tax advantages and other measures.

    _____ (d)   Businesses often merge with their competitors.

    _____ (e)   The small size of the Canadian market allows for the development of relatively few firms in some industries.

6. The number of corporate mergers and takeovers has increased sharply over the past decade. Three plausible reasons are

(a) _____

(b) _____

(c) _____

7. The traditional view is that the existence of big business tends to result in _____ prices and _____ output and _____ product quality than would be the case in competitive industries.

8. The most basic reason for the higher-than-average profit rates of oligopolists is that oligopolists

(a) are more efficient than average.

(b) advertise more than average.

(c) tend to avoid price competition.

(d) pay lower-than-average wages.

(e) pay a lower tax rate than smaller businesses.

9. State whether each of the following is a reason why the prices of oligopolists tend to be higher than they would he under competitive conditions.

_____ (a) Oligopolists' production methods are less efficient.

_____ (b) Oligopolists' advertising costs are higher.

_____ (c) Competitive industries almost all pay the minimum wage.

_____ (d) Oligopolists employ more people, and so have higher labour costs.

_____ (e) Oligopolists' profits are subject to particularly high tax rates, which force up their prices.

_____ (f) Oligopolists' profits are generally higher.

10. The prices of house brand or private label products in many supermarkets approximate the prices of similar goods under (competitive/oligopolistic) market conditions while the prices of brand name products more closely match prices under (competitive/oligopolistic) market conditions.

11. Write a description of the traditional view concerning the issue of bigness in business, and the appropriate government policy toward big business.

_____

_____

_____

_____

_____

_____

_____

_____

_____

_____

12. State whether each of the following is a reasonable argument in defence of bigness in business.

_____(a) The profits of big businesses (expressed as a rate of return on capital) are not higher than the profits of competitive industries.

_____(b) Oligopolists do not agree among themselves to raise prices and restrict output; rather, they compete vigorously on prices.

_____(c) Large corporations are more stable than smaller businesses, particularly with respect to maintaining employment during recessions.

_____(d) While abuses of big business' power (e.g., price-fixing) occurred in the past, these are now prevented by the anti-combines laws.

_____(e) Many criticisms of big businesses are vague and emotional rather than logical.

_____(f) Many oligopolistic corporations do not possess nearly the power to increase prices that their critics suggest.

_____(g) Big business tends to promote, rather than retard, technological progress.

_____(h)   Oligopolists constantly strive to improve the quality of their products to the maximum extent possible.

_____(i)   The reinvestment of the large profits of big business in research and development, technological change and capital investment raises productivity and thus society's standard of living.

13.   State whether each of the following statements concerning the ability of oligopolists to raise prices is **TRUE** or **FALSE**.

_____(a)   They have more ability to raise prices than do firms in "competitive" industries, but are limited by a variety of factors which often prevent them from raising prices and profits.

_____(b)   They have no freedom to raise prices, as all prices are determined by the government.

_____(c)   They possess the power to raise prices to any level they wish in order to maximize profits.

_____(d)   They could band together in order to raise prices and maximize profits if it were not for the anti-combines laws, which outlaw and thus prevent such practices.

_____(e)   They are usually unable to raise prices due to the fact that the demand for their products is nearly always very elastic.

14.   Five factors which limit the ability of oligopolists to raise prices are:

(a)   _____

(b)   _____

(c)   _____

(d)   _____

(e)   _____

15.   "Monopolistic (oligopolistic) corporations constitute a grave threat to the welfare of our society. The government should destroy them either by breaking them up into smaller units so as to increase competition, or by regulating them or by nationalizing them. Such action would greatly benefit the public."
Briefly explain how a representative of big business would reply to this statement.

_____

_____

_____

_____

_____

_____

_____

_____

_____

_____

_____

_____

16.   The dilemma Canada faces in determining its competition policy is that if more restrictions are placed on the growth of big business, there is the risk that Canadian businesses will be _____ _____ able to compete with foreign firms, whereas if government policy reduces restrictions on big business in order to avoid this problem, it creates the risk that consumers will be

_____

_____

17.   In 1996, Canada's largest bank was the _____.
Its proposed merger with the _____
was _____ by the federal government in 1998.

18. State whether the following would increase or decrease the market power of existing firms in the North American automobile industry.

A merger between GM and Ford _____

Reductiion of tariffs on imports of Japanese cars. _____

Bankruptcy, business shut down of Chrysler. _____

Development of a fuel cell (battery-operated) car by BMW. _____

A cartel agreement between current producers. _____

A worldwide recession. _____

19. In determining an appropriate competitive policy for Canada, what factors create a dilemma for Canadian authorities?

    (a) The profits of oligopolistic corporations in Canada are very much higher than in other countries, suggesting that price-fixing is a particularly serious problem in Canada.

    (b) The fact that Canada's largest corporations are much smaller than their foreign counterparts places them at a competitive disadvantage in international trade.

    (c) Industrial concentration in Canada is higher than in the United States and other countries.

    (d) (a) and (b) together.

    (e) (b) and (c) together.

20. It can be argued not only that the stronger laws against oligopolistic practices in general and mergers in particular would be beneficial to Canadians but also that such measures would be harmful to Canadians.

    Explain the facts and the arguments underlying the views that stronger laws against bigness in business would be: (a) in the best interests of Canadians, and (b) against the best interests of Canadians.

    _____

    _____

    _____

    _____

_____

_____

_____

_____

_____

_____

_____

_____

_____

_____

21.   The purpose of the Competition Act is to

   (a)   break up monopolies into small competing businesses.

   (b)   keep profit rates down to the average level.

   (c)   prevent takeovers of corporations by other corporations.

   (d)   prevent actions by businesses which unduly lessen competition and are
           thus detrimental to the consumer.

   (e)   all of the above.

22.   State whether the Competition Act outlaws the following:

   _____ (a)   One firm owning another firm in the same industry.

   _____ (b)   Mergers of firms that would unduly reduce competition.

   _____ (c)   Takeovers of firms by other firms.

   _____ (d)   Four or fewer firms having 50% or more of an industry's sales.

   _____ (e)   Price-fixing agreements among producers.

   _____ (f)   Various restrictive trade practices which reduce competition
                 unduly.

23.   The Competition Act is least effective against

   (a)   price-fixing.

   (b)   predatory pricing.

   (c)   mergers.

   (d)   resale price maintenance.

24.   Traditionally, Canadian trade policy has endeavoured to _____

_____

_____

25.   During the 1990s, international competition facing Canada became _____
with particular reference to competition from_____ and _____

26.   Growing competition from the United States is expected to result from

_____

_____

27.   The Competition Act allows firms to defend mergers on the grounds that the
proposed merger would likely result in _____
and thereby increase the ability of Canadian industry to _____.

28.   Competition Act violations generally involve single, clearly identifiable offenses
such as _____ or _____.

29.   Match the definitions on the right with the terms on the left.

	Laissez-faire	A	Lower production costs per unit made possible by higher volumes of production that permit the achievement of increased efficiencies.
	Marketing boards	B	The growing internationalization of business, trade, and finance that has characterized the period since the early 1980s.
	Industrial concentration	C	Consolidation of two or more companies through a purchase or pooling of interests, where a new company is formed to acquire the net assets of the combining companies.
	Economies of scale	D	The doctrine or philosophy that from the viewpoint of the public interest, it is neither necessary nor beneficial for governments to intervene in the operation of the economy.
	Globalization	E	Agreements among oligopolists to raise their prices above levels that would prevail in a competitive situation.
	Merger	F	Government-sponsored organizations of farmers that support farm incomes by restricting the supply of produce, usually through a system of quotas on individual farmers.
	Price-fixing	G	The degree to which an industry is dominated by a few terms.

Micro Chapter 10

Labour Markets and Labour Unions

This chapter focuses on the establishment of wage rates under differing labour market situations. Labour markets can be compared to product markets, in which the degree of control which sellers have over prices varies from highly competitive to monopolistic situations. Similarly, in labour markets, sellers have varying degrees of control over wages, ranging from highly organized skilled trade unions and professional groups to extremely open and competitive markets such as those for non-union part-time workers.

Non-union labour markets are explored, using the tools of supply, demand and elasticity. The effects of government interference with markets, in the form of price supports (minimum wage laws) are also analyzed.

The collective bargaining process is also examined, concluding with the assessment that this method of wage and benefit determination appears to work reasonably well in Canada.

General Learning Objective

Compare the operation of labour markets for both union and non-union workers.

Specific Learning Objectives

		Self-Test Reference
1.	Demonstrate the process of wage determination in the non-union sector of the labour market	#1-5
2.	Identify factors leading to wage differentials for labour in the non-union sector	#6
3.	Assess the impact of government wage legislation	#7,8
4.	Consider the extent of union organization in Canada	#9-12
5.	Recognize the legal aspects of a union work stoppage	#13-18

6. Identify forms of outside intervention in contract negotiations and
    labour disputes.   #19-21

7. Assess recent developments in Canadian industrial relations.   # 22,23

8. Review the key terms used in the chapter   #24

Self-Test

1. In the non-union sector of the labour force, wages and salaries are basically
    determined by

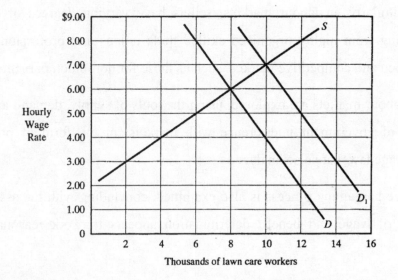

2. If the demand for lawn care workers is represented by the curve D, the hourly
    wage rate will be $___6___.

3. If the demand for lawn care workers increases, as shown by the curve D1, the
    hourly wage rate will be $___7___.

4. If the government set a minimum wage of $8.00 per hour for lawn care workers
    and the demand for these workers were represented by the curve D, the result
    would be ___Oversupply of 6000 workers___.

5. The market's adjustment to changes in demand will be smoother if the supply of
    labour is inelastic. TRUE or FALSE? Explain your answer.

    _____

    _____

    _____

    _____

6.   Economic theory would suggest that any differentials in wage rates that exist between different jobs would disappear as workers moved from low paying jobs to the higher pay jobs. However, wage rate differentials do exist from one job to another, even over long periods of time. Explain why this is so.

_____

_____

_____

_____

_____

7.   What is the economic impact of minimum wage legislation on labour markets?

_____

_____

_____

_____

_____

_____

_____

8.   In view of the economic impacts discussed above, explain why government would institute minimum wage legislation.

_____

_____

_____

_____

_____

_____

_____

9. By 2002, union membership in Canada amounted to less than _____ % of the civilian labour force.

10. In 1978, about _____ % of Canada's union members were women. By 2002, this percentage had increased to approximately _____ %.

11. Which of the following areas of employment is characterized by a relatively high degree of unionization?

   (a) government

   (b) manufacturing

   (c) service industries

   (d) construction

   (e) transportation

   (f) office/clerical

12. The decision whether to join a labour union (i.e., form a union "local") is made by

   _____

13. If an employer violates the terms of its contract (collective agreement) with its union (for instance, in the disciplining of employees), the union is legally empowered to _____

   _____

14. In Canada, a strike or lockout is legal

   (a) any time there is dispute between a union and an employer.

   (b) only after the contract has expired, the conciliation process has concluded and the cooling-off period required by the law has passed.

   (c) as soon as the conciliation process has concluded.

   (d) as soon as the existing contract (collective agreement) between the union and employer has expired.

   (e) none of the above.

15. Indicate whether each of the following statements regarding strikes is **TRUE** or **FALSE**.

   _____ (a) They are totally negative in character, they serve no useful purpose in our industrial relations system.

_____ (b)   They play an important role in our industrial relations system because the fear of a strike forces both the employer and the union to compromise in contract negotiations.

_____ (c)   Most employers would prefer a system in which strikes are outlawed and unresolved contract disputes are submitted to an arbitrator for a final decision.

_____ (d)   They impose very heavy economic costs on society in terms of lost output.

_____ (e)   Strikes by government employees constitute a more serious problem than strikes in the private sector.

16.   The proportion of union-management contract negotiations that is settled by negotiation and without a strike is generally _____ %.

17.   The percentage of total worker-hours worked in the Canadian economy that is lost due to strikes in recent years is _____.

18.   Which statement best describes the general attitudes of unions and management in the public service to a legal ban on all strikes?

(a)   Both favour outlawing strikes because this would eliminate costly strikes.

(b)   Employers generally favour such a move, but unions are reluctant to approve it.

(c)   Unions generally favour such a move, but employers are reluctant to approve it.

(d)   Both dislike such a move because it would require both of them to turn over to an arbitrator the right to decide issues of vital importance to them.

19.   Compulsory conciliation refers to:

(a)   the legal requirement that all unresolved grievances of workers (i.e., alleged violations of the collective agreement by the employer) be submitted to a referee for a final decision, to prevent strikes over them.

(b)   a procedure in which, by law, government-appointed official(s) must attempt to help employers and unions avoid a strike by reaching a negotiated agreement before a strike occurs.

(c)   a legal requirement that a government official from the Ministry of Labour must make final decisions on all disputes between unions and employers.

(d)   a procedure in which a government-appointed official makes a binding decision concerning a contract dispute involving a group of essential workers who cannot legally strike.

(e)   none of the above.

20.   Which of the following statements best describes the difference between "conciliation" and "arbitration"?

(a)   Arbitration is the process of attempting to help union and management reach an agreement; conciliation is an imposition of an agreement by a third party.

(b)   Arbitration is imposed to settle disputes that would otherwise result in a strike; conciliation is the process of filing a grievance against the employer by a worker.

(c)   Conciliation and arbitration are terms that mean essentially the same thing.

(d)   In a labour-management dispute, arbitration refers to the use of a neutral third party to make a decision that is binding on both sides; conciliation is a process whereby a neutral third party attempts to help the two sides reach an agreement.

21.   In public services which are considered to be essential, how are union-management disputes over contract negotiations resolved?

_____

_____

_____

22.   List three of the different trends which had emerged in Canadian industrial relations during the 1990s.

(1)   _____

(2)   _____

(3)   _____

23.   These changing trends have developed primarily because of

_____

_____

_____

24.   Match the definitions on the right with the terms on the left.

	Derived demand	A	The process through which workers deal as individuals with employers in negotiating terms and conditions of employment.
	Short run	B	The period of time after which the quantities of all inputs can be changed.
	Long run	C	The process through which unions and employers negotiate a new collective agreement.
	Minimum wage	D	A contract agreed upon by an employer and labour union, specifying the terms and conditions of employment of the employees for a specified period of time.
	Individual bargaining	E	The demand of a factor of production, which is generated (derived from) the demand for the good or service that is used to produced.
	Collective bargaining	F	An alleged violation of a collective agreement by an employer.
	Collective agreement	G	The resolution of union-management disputes by the decision of a third party.
	Compulsory conciliation	H	The period of time during which the quantities of some inputs cannot be changed.
	Grievance	I	A legal minimum wage rate set by law.
	Arbitration	J	A procedure, required by law before a strike is legal, in which a government-appointed officer (conciliator) attempts to help a union and employer to reach an agreement on the terms of a new collective agreement.

Micro Chapter 11

Employment and Incomes in the Canadian Economy

This chapter explores the trends in employment that are occurring in Canada and also income trends. Over the past four decades more and more Canadians are finding employment in the service industry (e.g. business and personal services, health care, education, finance, communications) while employment in the goods producing sector has grown very slowly. The reasons for this trend in employment are fully examined in the first part of this chapter.

The second part of the chapter analyzes income changes that Canadians are experiencing. Both family and per capita incomes are growing, but the distribution of total family incomes among the richest and poorest in society has remained remarkably stable. The issue of poverty in Canada is also discussed, including various concepts of what actually constitutes poverty, and how we identify the poor in society.

General Learning Objective

Observe the trends in employment resulting from changes in technology and demand, and examine the distribution of income in Canada with special attention to the problem of poverty.

Specific Learning Objectives

Self-Test

1.	Which of the following describes trends in the distribution of employment in Canada?

_____(a)	Employment in the service industries has been increasing faster than employment in the goods industries.

_____(b)	Blue-collar production workers have comprised a declining percentage of the labour force.

_____(c)	Agricultural employment has remained almost stable.

_____(d)	White-collar employment has been increasing faster than blue-collar employment.

_____(e)	Employment has been rising rapidly in the service industry sector of the economy.

2.	The changes in the labour force described in the preceding question have been largely caused by

(a)	_____

_____

(b)	_____

_____

3.	The changes in demand for labour in the manufacturing and agricultural sectors has resulted from

(a)	fewer agricultural and manufacturing goods being demanded by consumers.

(b)   an increase in the demand for manufactured products, but a decrease in the demand for agricultural products.

(c)   the extensive technological changes that have altered production methods in manufacturing and agriculture.

(d)   all of the above.

4.   As living standards increase, Canadians tend to

(a)   Spend more on services, thereby creating employment opportunities in service industries.

(b)   Increase consumption of food products, creating more jobs in agriculture.

(c)   Reduce their spending on manufactured goods.

(d)   Spend their increases proportionately on food products, manufactured goods, and services.

5.   Which of the following are consequences of changing production technology, more consumer spending on services, and many more women entering the work force?

_____ (a)   urbanization of society

_____ (b)   decreasing living standards

_____ (c)   rising educational requirements for workers

_____ (d)   larger families

_____ (e)   decreased immigration

_____ (f)   growth of part time work

6.   The danger of jobs being lost as a result of technological changes is often offset by the following:

(a)   _____

(b)   _____

7.   **TRUE** or **FALSE?**

_____(a)   A key to adapting to change is education and training.

_____(b)   For society in general, investment in producing a high quality labor force tends to attract job-creating business investment.

_____(c)   A key strength of Canadian education for the workforce is its high attainment of basic literacy and numeracy skills.

_____(d)   In Canada the supply of skilled workers has been sufficient to meet the demand for skilled workers.

8.   Between the 1950s and the 1970s, average real family incomes in Canada increased substantially due to

(a)   lower unemployment.

(b)   more adherence to stricter work quotas.

(c)   rising worker productivity.

(d)   an increase in the number of income earners per family.

(e)   both (c) and (d) above are correct.

9.   After the late 1970's, growth of average real income per family slowed because of _____ and _____.

10.   In Canada, by the year 2000, the top 20% of families received roughly ____ % of the total income, while the bottom 20% received about _____ % of total income.

11.   Studies indicate that women earn about _____% of what men earn for full-time work.

12.   The difference between incomes of men and women is partly explained by economic factors such as _____ and by productivity factors including _____, _____, and _____.

13.   The major gender factor explaining the male-female wage gap is referred to as

_____.

14.   (a)   The five occupational groups in which approximately three-quarters of female employees work are (1) _____ (2)_____ (3)_____(4)_____ (5)_____.

(b)   Explain how these occupational groups affect the average income of women in general.

_____

15,   Within the concept of "equal pay for equal value," explain what is meant by "work of equal value."

_____

16.   An official poverty line based on Statistics Canada's low income cut-offs would
       include

       (a)   all families in the lowest 40% of income earners.

       (b)   all families with a total income below $20 000 per year.

       (c)   all families whose income is less than half the national average family
              income.

       (d)   all families that spend more than 56.2% of their income on basic
              necessities.

17.   According to the LICO's based Statistics Canada poverty line, approximately
       _____ Canadians live in poverty.

18.   What is the major criticism of the use of LICO's as a measure of poverty?
       _____

19.   Explain how the "Market Basket Measure" (MBM) poverty lines differ from the
       LICO based poverty lines.
       _____

20.   According to the 1998 MBM-based definition of poverty adopted by Canadian
       governments, a family of four would be considered poor if it was unable to buy or
       rent

       (a)   _____

       (b)   _____

       (c)   _____

       (d)   _____

21.   The adoption of the MBM poverty lines caused the poverty rate in Canada to

       (a)   increase by about 1.5 million people.

       (b)   drop by 20%.

       (c)   drop by nearly one third.

       (d)   increase by about one-third.

22.   Among all family types, the subcategory with the highest poverty rate is
       _____.

23.   Match the definitions on the right with the terms on the left.

	Poverty line	A	Expresses how the nation's income is shared among members of the population.
	Low income cut-off	B	The concept that values of different jobs may be measured against each other using a point system.
	Market basket measure	C	Families below this level spend 46.2 percent of more of their income on food, clothing and shelter.
	National council of Welfare	D	The percentage of people who are considered to be poor.
	Poverty rate	E	Income level below which families are considered to be poor.
	Equal pay for work of equal value	F	People are considered poor if their income is far below the average income.
	Income distribution	G	Money given to people (not in exchange for a good or service).
	Physical definition of poverty	H	Poverty line based on the cost of a "basket" of goods and services that a family requires to live above the poverty line.
	Labour force participation rate	I	Unable to afford the necessities of life.
	Transfer payment	J	A citizens' advisory board on matters of concern to low-income Canadians
	Relative (social) definition of poverty.	K	The percentage of working age people who work or desire to work.

Micro Chapter 12

The Government Sector

This chapter deals with all three levels of government in Canada, including the economic roles of government, as well as revenues and expenditures. The focus is on the period from 1950 to the present.

For almost half a century, the growth of the role of government generally was regarded as beneficial, because it remedied economic problems and, thus, yielded favourable results. However, more recently, increases in government spending, taxation and borrowing came to be associated with the deteriorating performance of the economy. Thus serious concerns were raised over the extent of government involvement in the economy and the size of the federal deficit.

Since 1950 the incomes that Canadians earned grew more than 40-fold, from $17 billion in 1950 to roughly $800 billion in 2001. Government expenditures, however, grew at an even greater pace. For instance, in 1950 nearly 22% of all earned wealth passed through the hands of government; in 2001 government handled roughly 40% of this wealth. However, a large portion of these funds was not actually spent by government to procure goods and services; rather, it was re-distributed through social programs for others to spend. Unfortunately, slow growth rates in the 1970s and 1980s coupled with the rising emphasis on social programs led to deficits because government expenditures rose faster than revenues from taxes. This situation led governments to reduce their commitments to social programs, which they accomplished in the decade of the 1990s. At the same time, however, economic growth sped up. As a result revenues have exceeded expenditures in the past few years, leaving surpluses.

This chapter discusses the trends in government revenues and expenditures and their fiscal implications, in four major topic areas: types of government expenditure, types of tax revenues, the impacts of redistributing money, and a fifty-year perspective on deficits and surpluses.

General Learning Objective

Identify the nature of government involvement in today's economy.

Specific Learning Objectives

Self-Test

1. Total spending by all levels of government in Canada rose dramatically from _____ percent of GDP 1950 to ___ percent 1992. However, it then declined to about ___ percent in 2001. These statistics exclude the contribution of _____ corporations.

2. The key economic roles of government are: _____,
_____, and _____.

3. Regulation, as it applies to the economy, may be defined as _____
_____
_____

4.   The three largest categories of government spending in Canada (for all three levels of government combined) are:

(a)   _____

(b)   _____

(c)   _____

5.   Which of the following is not an example of an income security program?

(a)   Guaranteed income supplement

(b)   Child Tax Benefit

(c)   Quebec Pension Plan

(d)   Canada Savings Bond Interest

(e)   Employment Insurance

6.   Which taxpayer is likely to benefit least from the application of a tax credit?

(a) A person with many children.

(b) A person with a high marginal tax rate.

(c) A person with a low marginal tax rate.

7.   List eight reasons for the substantial growth in spending on income security, health care and education programs over the last few decades.

(a)   _____

(b)   _____

(c)   _____

(d)   _____

(e)   _____

(f)   _____

(g)   _____

(h)   _____

8.   By far the greatest portion of government expenditures is on _____ _____ programs.

9.   The objective of adopting the tax credit system was to _____

10.   State whether each of the following statements is **TRUE** or **FALSE**.

_____(a)   The federal government lacks the taxing authority to raise sufficient revenues to finance all of its expenditures.

_____(b) Federal government spending has in recent decades expanded more rapidly than has spending by provincial and municipal governments.

_____(c) Generally, provincial governments tend to be the wealthiest of all three levels of government.

_____(d) City governments are very severely strained financially due to their extensive spending requirements and their very limited authority to levy taxes.

_____(e) The federal government is responsible for funding education, health and welfare programs throughout Canada.

_____(f) The federal government has shown an interest in reducing its expenditures on health care and education by limiting increases to the rate of increase in GNP.

11. Ernie, an accountant, earns $30 000 per year, on which he pays income tax of $7000. If Ernie takes on extra work as a night school teacher, he will earn an additional $6000, on which he will pay additional income taxes of $1800. From this, we can conclude that Ernie's marginal tax rate is _____%.

12. Generally speaking, high marginal tax rates tend to
(a)   reduce the incentive to work.
(b)   not affect the incentive to work.
(c)   reduce the incentive to save and invest.
(d)   (a) and (c) together.
(d) increase the incentive to work.

13. When all taxes are considered, Canada's tax system is quite progressive. **TRUE** or **FALSE**? Why?_____

_____

_____

14. In 1991, the federal government introduced the _____ to replace the existing federal tax on manufactured goods.

15. Governments can raise tax revenues (generally) by taxing _____, _____, and _____.

16. The impact of a sales tax is particularly burdensome for _____ income people. Such taxes are _____ taxes.

17. Discuss major advantages and disadvantages of federal sales taxes.

_____

_____

_____

_____

_____

_____

18. The stated objective of the Goods and Services Tax was _____

_____

19. The following table illustrates several of the stages of production for an automobile. Based on a 7% GST fill in the blanks under the Tax, Rebate, and Net Tax columns.

Seller	Buyer	Price	Tax	Rebate	Net Tax
Iron Ore Producer	Steel Producer	$ 1000	_____	_____	_____
Steel Producer	Car Manufacturer	5000	_____	_____	_____
Car Manufacturer	Car Dealer	10 000	_____	_____	_____
Car Dealer	Consumer	16 000	_____	_____	_____

20. Excessively high tax rates on business profits can reduce _____

_____.

21. Four basic criticisms of Canada's social welfare system are:

(a) _____

(b) _____

(c) _____

(d) _____

22.   State whether each of the following statements regarding Canada's welfare system is **TRUE** or **FALSE**.

_____(a)   If the bureaucracy supporting Canada's welfare system were eliminated, every Canadian household below the poverty line could potentially receive an annual subsidy in excess of an annual minimum wage income.

_____(b)   The principle of universality ensures that all Canadians can share equally in the benefits accrued from Canada's health care programs.

_____(c)   Generally, it encourages welfare recipients to seek work.

_____(d)   Employment insurance contributes to high-unemployment and low-wage regions.

_____(e)   An increase in the minimum wage rate can actually contribute to unemployment by encouraging labour-force drop-outs to seek work.

23.   The major way in which our welfare system reduces the incentive of welfare recipients to work is that:

(a)   welfare benefits are so high that many people actually gain greatly economically by quitting work and going on welfare.

(b)   people on welfare are not permitted to seek work.

(c)   welfare agencies and social workers encourage people to remain on welfare rather than to seek employment.

(d)   there are no government agencies to help those on welfare to find employment.

(e)   if a welfare recipient earns money by working, his/her welfare is reduced by so much that he/she has little economic incentive to work.

24.   Describe the net effect of government programs (including both taxes and government spending) on the distribution of income among Canadian families.

_____

_____

_____

_____

_____

_____

_____

_____

_____

25.   During the 1980's, Canada's rising debt and its contributing deficits became a

       concern to many Canadians because:

       (a)   _____

       (b)   _____

       (c)   _____

       (d)   _____

              _____

26.   State whether each of the following suggestions could serve as a possible means

       of reducing a government's deficit.

       _____ (a)   Target social expenditures to those who need them the most.

       _____ (b)   Offer incentives to save, work and invest.

       _____ (c)   Consumption taxes

       _____ (d)   Implement a national guaranteed minimum income program.

       _____ (e)   Increase eligibility requirements and reduce benefits.

27.   A major obstacle to proposed reductions in spending in the areas of pensions and

       Employment insurance has been _____

28.   Elimination of the 1992–93 total government deficits would have required a

       _____ % increase in personal income taxes.

29.   Rather than imposing massive tax increases, governments sought to reduce their

       deficits by _____

30.   "The only really effective way to combat poverty in Canada is to increase taxes

       on the rich dramatically so as to provide the funds required for massive

       redistribution of income from the rich to the poor."

       TRUE or **FALSE**? Why? _____

       _____

       _____

31.   "We do not believe that the funds necessary to maintain and improve these
        programs cannot be found. The federal government did not need to spend more
        than $1 billion for the bank bailout. It did not have to give more than $2 billion in
        capital gains exemptions and other tax breaks, which favour the healthy and
        wealthy. It gave more than $1.6 billion in corporate income tax reductions and
        another $3.3 billion to increase defense spending by 35% by 1990-91. We believe
        a just and fair tax system would provide the money necessary, not only to
        maintain post-secondary education and health programs at present levels, but to
        provide more than enough to bring them up to the standard in many of the
        developed countries of this world."

                                                                David Orlikow, MP
                                                                Winnipeg. North
                                                                House of Commons Debate
                                                                June 12, 1986

        AGREE or **DISAGREE**?

        _____

        _____

        _____

        _____

        _____

        _____

32.   The three main alternatives that the federal government has considered for federal
        budget surpluses that developed after 1997 were to _____,
        _____, or _____.

33.   Former Prime Minister Cretien had been criticized for spending too little on the
        Canadian military.   The Prime Minister replied that Canadians preferred that the
        government spend more money on health care. Explain how this debate involves
        an opportunity cost.

        _____

        _____

        _____

34.   Match the definitions on the right with the terms on the left.

	Gross Domestic Product (GDP)	A	The total amount borrowed (and owing) by the federal government.
	Tax credit	B	A tax that takes a higher percentage of a higher income than of a lower income.
	Consumption tax	C	A measure of the goods and services produced within a country.
	Progressive tax	D	A tax that applies to the last dollar of one's taxable income.
	Marginal tax rate	E	Government imposed constraint on economic behaviour.
	Regressive tax	F	An excess of planned spending over revenues.
	Payroll tax	G	Employment insurance or CPP premiums are examples of this tax.
	Budget deficit	H	Charges to users of government services.
	User fees	I	Excess of revenue over planned expenditure
	Federal debt	J	Reduces a person's income tax to offset certain living costs.
	Regulation	K	A tax levied on good purchased (e.g. GST).
	Fiscal	L	A tax that takes a higher percentage of a lower income than of a higher income; it is a fixed fee.
	Budget surplus	M	The budget for a year's period.

Micro Chapter 13

THE POLITICS OF ECONOMICS

This chapter examines the relationship between politics and economics. Discussion focuses on two different philosophies, which usually are described as "right-wing" or "left-wing" and how these philosophies apply to economic issues.

The main beliefs of both sides are described, indicating that right-wingers generally favour the operation of free markets, while left-wingers lack faith in free markets as a means of achieving prosperity.

Left-wing perspectives on economic issues are contrasted with the right-wing perspectives, with particular reference to business enterprise, profits, investment income, the distribution of income, social welfare, labour unions, the role of government, and political realities.

General Learning Objective

Distinguish between right-wing and left-wing philosophies as applied to specific economic issues.

Specific Learning Objectives

Self-Test

1. Right-wingers exhibit a strong belief in

   (a) _____

   (b) _____

   (c) _____

2. Therefore, the best solution to economic problems, for a right-winger, is provided through

   _____

3. For right-wingers, economic efficiency is achieved through the functioning of the _____ motive.

4. Left-wingers maintain that the free market system is biased in favour of

   _____

5. Left-wingers argue that the benefits of capitalist economies accrue to

   _____

6. To counteract this problem, left-wingers advocate _____

   _____

   _____

7. A more collective approach to economic issues is stressed by the _____ wingers.

8. Profits are viewed as an incentive for efficiency by the _____ wingers.

9. Relatively heavy taxation of profits is favoured by _____ wingers.

10. Right-wingers maintain that income from financial investments provides

    _____

    _____

    _____

11. The _____ wingers consider that consumer sovereignty is an important factor in deciding what gets produced.

12.   Left-wingers argue that incomes (do/do not) measure people's contribution to society.

13.   Left-wingers believe government should redistribute incomes through the use of _____ and _____.

14.   Labour unions generally find greater support among the _____ wingers, because _____

    _____

    _____

    _____

    _____

15.   Left-wingers favour government policies to protect workers and consumers against _____

16.   A continued growth of government and policies to redistribute income and regulate business is considered by right-wingers as a move toward

    _____.

17.   A laissez-faire approach falls within the realm of the _____ wingers.

18.   Excessive government borrowing tends to _____ interest rates, which _____ business capital investment and _____ economic growth.

19.   Suggest three main dangers to society that may result from following an extreme right-wing approach:

    (a)   _____

    (b)   _____

    (c)   _____

20.   Dangers inherent to society from following an extreme left-wing approach include:

    (a)   _____

    (b)   _____

    (c)   _____

21.   The long-term trend has been toward the _____ wing position.

22.   By the mid-1980s federal policy in Canada had become more _____ wing in nature.

23.   By the mid-1980s, the federal government in Canada was directing its efforts to control _____, while at the same time trying to improve
_____

24.   During the 1990s, the federal government reacted to a federal debt crisis by

(a)   raising taxes.

(b)   borrowing heavily in foreign markets.

(c)   selling government assets.

(d)   carrying out major reductions in program spending.

25.   How have right wingers and left wingers approached the debate about health care in Canada at the beginning of the new millennium?

_____

_____

_____

_____

_____

_____

_____

_____

_____

_____

_____

_____

_____

26.   Match the definitions on the right with the terms on the left.

	Efficiency	A	Philosophy that production should be privately owned.
	Income distribution	B	Measure of how income is shared between different income groups.
	Capitalism	C	A key assumption or "law" about how things work.
	Philosophy	D	Measure of performance in terms of cost per unit.
	Principle	E	A way of thinking about ethics or principles of living.

Micro Chapter 14

ENVIRONMENTAL ECONOMICS

Environment problems have been with us for decades and pollution in particular is not a recent phenomenon. But it was during the late sixties and the early seventies that environmental awareness and concern about pollution began to surface as a major public concern. Governments across Canada joined the crusade to "save the environment" and initiated steps to try and protect it. The majority of politicians responded to our concerns by passing environmental legislation of one sort or another. Many provinces went one step further and created quasi-judicial agencies to fight and/or regulate polluters.

With the economic problems of severe inflation in the late 1970s and unemployment in the 1980s, environmental issues were relegated to a lesser role. Only of late has the environment emerged as a major public issue.

Unfortunately, Canadians still seem to be preoccupied with who's to blame, rather than focusing on causes and remedies. There are still strong incentives to pollute and only recently has government been prepared to take any really serious action against polluters. Canadians want a cleaner environment and they may be ready to incur the costs of a clean-up. Many Canadians are becoming more proactive in trying to take action to protect the environment. The consequences of not doing so are becoming more and more apparent.

General Learning Objective

Explore the nature of environmental concerns confronting Canada today.

Specific Learning Objectives

Self-Test

1.   Two factors which have combined to bring environmental problems into the forefront of public concern during the second half of the 1980s are

_____ and _____.

2.   Define

    (a)   private costs _____

        _____

    (b)   social costs _____

        _____

3.   Which of the following is an example of a social cost?

    (a)   wages, salaries, rents, dividends

    (b)   leasehold improvements

    (c)   The effects of nitrous oxide emissions from transport vehicles

    (d)   interest payments on corporate bonds

4.   While attempting to minimize its internal costs, a socially responsible producer would want to (minimize/maximize) its external costs.

5.   An externality is defined as _____

_____

6.   Which of the following are examples of externalities?

     _____(a)   loud rock or blue grass music

     _____(b)   sulphur emissions from the stack of a metal refinery

     _____(c)   exhaust emissions from automobiles

     _____(d)   dust released from a concrete plant

     _____(e)   animal feed produced as a by-product from an ethanol plant

7.   In attempting to maximize its profits by cutting costs, a producer may determine that

     (a)   minimizing social costs is a less important objective than minimizing private costs.

     (b)   private cost structures should be replaced by social costs.

     (c)   social costs should be replaced by private costs.

     (d)   (a) and (b) above.

8.   The concept of a trade-off between consumer goods production and environmental preservation implies that

     (a)   increases in consumer goods production will cause environmental damage.

     (b)   more consumer goods production will be accompanied by a cleaner environment:

     (c)   a cleaner environment can be achieved without sacrificing any production of consumer goods.

     (d)   to achieve an increasingly cleaner environment, society will encounter constant cost increases.

9.   Cost-benefit analysis can help regulators to determine

     (a)   _____

     (b)   _____

     (c)   _____

10.   **TRUE** or **FALSE**?

_____ (a)   It is the responsibility of economists who conduct cost-benefit analyses to recommend specific courses of action to reduce environmental damage.

_____ (b)   Cost-benefit analysis is useful to environmental studies in that it provides estimates of the gains and losses resulting from pollution.

_____ (c)   The question of deciding who should pay for a particular program to correct an environmental problem may be partly answered through cost-benefit analysis.

_____ (d)   The traditional market forces, which attach a price to all private goods, will provide the most satisfactory solution to the problem of environmental damage.

11.   In the past generation, global environmental problems have become recognized, including: _____, _____ and _____.

12.   The main objective of government anti-pollution policy should be to

(a)   force all pollution costs to be external.

(b)   reduce all external costs to zero.

(c)   transfer external costs to the polluter's internal cost structure.

(d)   transfer the pollution costs from the user of the product to the producer of the product.

13.   Point out the main problem(s) encountered when government adopts the following anti-pollution actions:

(a)   Direct regulation, i.e., the setting of minimum standards that a firm must meet: _____

_____

_____

(b)   Levying a tax on polluters: _____

_____

_____

(c)   Providing victims of pollution with the opportunity to sue the polluters for damages: _____

_____

_____

(d)   Tradable pollution credits: _____

_____

_____

14.   Under what circumstances might it be appropriate for government to subsidize a firm's cost of installing pollution-control equipment?

_____

_____

15.   Of the three methods of handling household and industrial waste, the least costly is

(a)   the use of landfills.

(b)   incineration.

(c)   recycling.

(d)   all methods cost about the same.

16.   Which of the following statements concerning recycling are correct?

_____(a)   It is by far the most economical method of dealing with waste.

_____(b)   Most recycling schemes have proven to be highly profitable.

_____(c)   Large quantities of recycled materials that have been collected have tended to drive their market prices to very low levels.

_____(d)   Recycling has been a very popular concept with the public and their governments.

_____(e)   It is often more economical for producers to use virgin raw materials than recycled materials.

_____(f)   Market forces for raw materials are a major factor in projecting the success of recycling programs.

17.   What initiatives might householders be expected to take, if a charge were levied on each bag of garbage that is picked up? _____

_____

18.	The "greenhouse effect" is caused mainly by the emissions of _____ gas. This gas is caused by the burning of _____, of which the largest single user is the _____. Therefore, to reduce the threat of an emerging greenhouse effect, it would be reasonable to recommend that people

	_____.

19.	How does public concern with environmental problems change as the economy moves from boom periods to recession? Explain the connection between the health of the economy and environmental concerns.

	_____

	_____

	_____

	_____

	_____

	_____

	_____

	_____

	_____

20.	Match the term on the right with the definition on the left.

	Private (internal) cost	A	Contamination of the environment with materials that inhibit health and the quality of life.
	Social (external) cost	B	After a certain point, productivity reduces as additional units are produced.
	Diminishing returns	C	Agreement by several countries to deal with substances that deplete the ozone layer.
	Kyoto protocol	D	Costs of production that are passed on to society as a whole.
	Greenhouse effect	E	Production cost paid by the producer.
	Pollution	F	Certain gases released into the atmosphere contribute to global warming.
	Economic tradeoff	G	The need to give up one thing to get something else, due to limited resources.

Micro Chapter 15

THE AGRICULTURAL SECTOR

Although only 3% of Canadian workers are employed in primary agriculture, this sector has traditionally been, and continues to be, of great importance to Canadians. Agricultural exports are worth billions of dollars to the Canadian economy, contributing to a favourable foreign trade balance.

Even as the number of farms in Canada decreases and fewer Canadians live on farms, the industry continues to be highly competitive. Larger, more highly mechanized farms have resulted in huge increases in productivity. Since less labour is required to operate our primary agriculture sector, more workers are available for employment in other industries.

In spite of the agricultural revolution of the twentieth century, farm operators are still beset with economic difficulties, many of which result from the competitive nature of this industry. This chapter addresses problems faced by producers, much of the analysis involving the familiar tools of supply, demand, and elasticity.

General Learning Objective

Analyze the problems facing agricultural producers and consider a number of possible solutions.

Specific Learning Objectives

	Self-Test Reference
1. Recognize the importance of Canada's agricultural sector	#1-2
2. Point out the impacts of Canada's agricultural revolution	#3- 4

3. Analyze the reasons for "low" farm incomes. .... #5-8

4. Use the concept of elasticity to explain the instability of farm incomes. .... #9-10

5. Show how each of the following programs apply to the "farm problem:" .... #11-15

        a. Offers to purchase.

        b. Acreage restriction

        c. Deficiency payments.

6. Identify the scale of direct payment programs to Canadian farmers. ....#16

7. Critique the role of agricultural marketing boards. .... #17-18

8. Discuss the merits of government support programs for agriculture................. #19-20

9. Compare the use of marketing boards with the use of deficiency payments............ #21

10. Review the key terms used in the chapter..#22

Self-Test

1.   Canada's farming industry consists mainly of

    (a)   medium-sized corporations.

    (b)   sole proprietors, who own the land they work.

    (c)   partnerships of land owners and farm operators.

    (d)   large incorporated farm businesses.

2.   Agricultural production in Canada is important in that it

    (a)   contributes nearly 4% of our total output and produces a valuable source of exports.

    (b)   generates over 20% of our total output, and 25% of our total employment.

    (c)   produces an ever increasing share of our total output.

    (d)   provides a very stable income to many thousands of people.

3.   As a result of the Agricultural Revolution of the twentieth century,

    (a)   the number of farms in Canada has increased.

    (b)   fewer people now live on farms.

    (c)   productivity on farms has increased.

    (d)   a lower proportion of Canada's labour force is now required on farms.

    (e)   (b), (c), (d) above.

4.   The effects of the Agricultural Revolution on Canada's economy are generally considered to be

(a)   unfavourable, as they have added to our unemployment problem.

(b)   beneficial, in that they have allowed workers to be transferred from agricultural production to industrial production.

(c)   neutral, in that they have benefited one sector of our economy, at the expense of another.

(d)   of little consequence, since agricultural output is no longer an important part of our total output.

5.   Which of the following describes the historical farm problem?

(a)   Farm efficiency has been high, but farm prices and incomes have been low.

(b)   Farm prices and incomes have been unstable, with a tendency to decline sharply periodically.

(c)   Both (a) and (b) above.

(d)   Low efficiency and high-cost-per-unit operations have caused profit margins to be narrow and farm incomes to be low.

(e)   Because farm efficiency has steadily improved, profit margins and farm incomes have risen faster than those in other industries.

6.   State whether each of the following has been a factor contributing to the problem(s) referred to in the previous question.

_____(a)   Farm technology has not improved significantly over the past 50 years.

_____(b)   Farming is a highly competitive industry.

_____(c)   Because Canadian farms have been small by international standards, they have lagged behind foreign competitors in efficiency, and thus suffered from foreign competition.

_____(d)   Both the supply of and demand for food tend to be relatively inelastic.

_____(e)   Variations in weather conditions cause the supply of many types of food to fluctuate considerably from year to year.

ANSWER THE FOLLOWING FOUR QUESTIONS ON THE BASIS OF THE
FOLLOWING GRAPH:

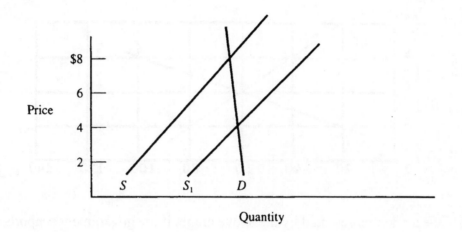

7.   In the graph above, the change in supply represented by the shift from S to S1
        would be caused by

        (a)   higher prices for wheat.

        (b)   a larger crop of wheat.

        (c)   a smaller crop of wheat.

        (d)   lower prices for wheat.

8.   The change in supply from S to S1 would cause the price of wheat to change from
        $ _____ to $_____ and cause farm incomes to _____.
        But if supply were to shift from S1 to S as a result of a major drought then some
        farm incomes would _____.

9.   This fluctuation in price is as large as it is because:

        (a)   demand for food is inelastic and the supply of food is unstable.

        (b)   demand for food is elastic and the supply of food is stable.

        (c)   demand for food has decreased in relation to supply.

        (d)   the demand for food is usually unstable.

        (e)   the supply of food is unusually stable

10.   If the demand for wheat were more elastic, fluctuations in its price would be

        _____.

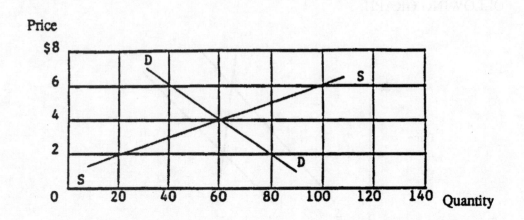

11.   In the market represented by the above graph, if the government supports the

        price of product B at $6 by means of offers to purchase, the result will be

        _____.

12.   To avoid the situation described in the previous question, governments in some

        cases _____.

13.   Which of the following accurately describes the operation of a system of

        deficiency payments?

        _____ (a)   The government abandons all attempts to support farm incomes

                      and lets them be determined freely in the marketplace, even if

                      prices are deficient.

        _____ (b)   The government does not buy surpluses or restrict farm output, but

                      rather ensures through direct subsidies to farmers that they receive

                      a predetermined price for their crops.

        _____ (c)   The government sets up marketing boards which allocate quotas to

                      individual farmers to ensure that prices are high enough to yield

                      reasonable returns to the average farmer without generating

                      surpluses of farm products.

        _____ (d)   The government offers to buy farm products at predetermined

                      prices and absorbs via these purchases any surpluses which may

                      occur.

_____ (e)   The government guarantees farmers 90% of the average price over the past 5 years for their crops.

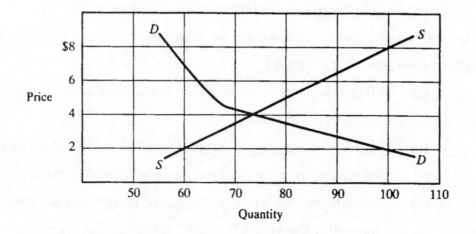

14.   If a system of deficiency payments were applied to the product B market represented by the above graph, with a target price of $8, the output of product B will be _____ units and the market price will be $_____ per unit.

15.   Under the deficiency payments program described in the previous questions, the government's obligation would be to _____

_____

16.   Between 1986 and 1995, direct payments by government accounted for what per cent of farmers' net incomes?

    (a)   25%

    (b)   50%

    (c)   60%

    (d)   75%

    (e)   90%

17.   The purpose of marketing boards is to _____

_____

18.   Indicate whether each of the following is a criticism that has been made of marketing boards.

    _____ (a)   They have failed to increase either farm prices or incomes.

    _____ (b)   Their monopolistic power has resulted in higher than competitive market prices.

_____ (c)   They limit the expansion of farms into larger, more efficient units.

_____ (d)   They have resulted in windfall profits for some producers.

_____ (e)   They keep small, inefficient farms in operation.

19.   Indicate whether each of the following can reasonably be argued in defense of government assistance to farmers.

_____ (a)   These programs ensure that Canada will have a healthy agricultural sector in the future.

_____ (b)   These programs help to preserve farm land which otherwise might be sold for industrial, commercial or residential purposes.

_____ (c)   Since farmers are much more exposed to economic insecurity than most other Canadians, it is "fair" to provide farmers with government assistance when it is needed.

_____ (d)   It is economically desirable to keep as large a proportion of the population as possible employed in the agricultural sector.

20.   As the decade of the 1990s ended many Canadian grain growers were suffering devastating losses as a direct result of subsidies paid to European and American grain producers by their governments.

Using demand, supply analysis, explain and illustrate graphically how foreign subsidy programs adversely affect Canadian farm incomes.

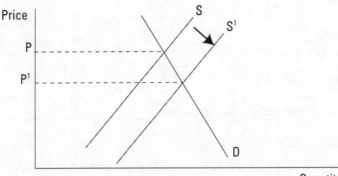

_____
_____
_____
_____
_____
_____
_____
_____

21.   If food shortages became a general concern in the future, which of the following
       would be the most logical way to provide assistance to farmers in those cases in
       which this was necessary?

       (a)   marketing boards

       (b)   acreage restriction

       (c)   deficiency payments

       (d)   offers to purchase

       (e)   any of the above — none would be more advantageous than the others

       Explain the reason for your answer _____

       _____

       _____

       _____

22. Match the definitions on the right with the terms on the left.

	Agricultural revolution.	A	Encourages farmers to leave land uncultivated.
	"Farm problem"	B	Reference to the impact of technological change of farm productivity.
	"Offer to Purchase" stabilization program	C	Government pays farmers the difference between the market price and a higher "target" price.
	"Acreage restriction" crop management program	D	A measure of output per worker.
	"Deficiency payment" farm support program	E	A group of nations who negotiate rules for world wide international trade.
	Agricultural marketing board	F	Payment from government to a producer to reduce the producer's cost of manufacture.
	World Trade Organization	G	Characterizes the combination of low and unstable income experienced by farmers.
	Productivity	H	Government guarantees the purchase of agricultural product at a specified price.
	Subsidy	I	Organization of farmers with the legal right to restrict the production of member firms in their industry.

Micro Chapter 16

INTO THE FUTURE

Since the late 1980's, the world has experienced a major increase in international trade. This, combined with increased competition and a significantly greater mobility of capital, has brought about a "globalization" of world markets. As a consequence of these developments, Canada has had to rethink its approach to economic development. The old strategy of relying on the extraction of rich natural resources and protecting an inefficient manufacturing industry was becoming incompatible with the new realities.

As part of the changing world order, third world countries, notably in Asia and Latin America, as well as in the emerging market economies of Eastern Europe, were rapidly acquiring industrial and technological expertise, enabling them to become tough, aggressive, and efficient new competitors in international markets.

Canada faced the options of either attempting to insulate and isolate itself from these new competitive forces, or adapting itself to a rapidly changing world. If the latter option were to be followed it was evident that new economic policies and new directions would be required.

General Learning Objective

Evaluate Canada's strategies for improving its competitive position in world markets.

Specific Learning Objectives

	Self-Test Reference
1. Recognize Canada's traditional sources of economic prosperity.	#1
2. Identify the challenges for Canada to create wealth in this decade	#2-4

3. Distinguish between various economic policies of the government. ....#5

4. Review the key terms used in the chapter. ....#6

Self-Test

1.   Canada's traditional source of economic prosperity was in the

    (a)   export of manufactured goods.

    (b)   export of raw materials.

    (c)   inflow of foreign business capital investment.

    (d)   establishment of social welfare programs.

    (e)   (b) and (c) above.

2.   Describe the main factors that contributed to the major increases in world trade in

    the 1980s and 1990s. _____

    _____

    _____

3.   The major problem facing Canada as a consequence of the emergence of a global

    economy in the 1980s was: _____

    _____

    _____

    _____

4.   In selecting a manufacturing site for a high-technology industry, the most

    important consideration for the business firm is

    (a)   a cheap source of raw material.

    (b)   low wage rates.

    (c)   both (a) and (b) above.

    (d)   the presence of a skilled work force with the required specialized

        knowledge.

5.   Match each of the following government policy initiatives undertaken in the 1980s and 1990s (#1-8, Column A) with the intended results (Column B):

A

1. The 1989 Free Trade Agreement with the United States

2. Action to keep inflation at a low level

3. Tax reform

4. Deregulation of industry

5. Changes to the competition legislation

6. Reductions in government subsidies to business

7. Changes to the Unemployment Insurance system

8. Investment in human resources

B

_____ (a) to improve efficiency rather than relying on government handouts

_____ (b) to keep prices competitive and interest rates low

_____ (c) to put emphasis on productivity, competitiveness, and internationalism

_____ (d) to promote a knowledge-based economy

_____ (e) an attempt to increase incentives to work, save, and invest

_____ (f) to make it more difficult for business to reduce competition through mergers or price-fixing agreements

6.   Match the definitions on the right with the terms on the left.

	"Resource wealth mentality"	A	Reduces the rules that government imposes on an industry.
	Deregulation	B	View that wealth is derived from the sale of natural resources.
	Efficiency	C	Using the least cost combination of resources to produce an item.
	Productivity	D	Corporation owned by the government.
	Privatization	E	A payment from government to a producer for the purpose of lowering the producer's cost.
	Subsidy	F	The transfer of government operations and assets to the private sector
	Crown Corporation	G	A measure of output per worker.

Micro Answers

Chapter 1

1.   (d)

2.   is not; it deals with the behavior of people, which cannot be scientifically analyzed or predicted.

3.   False statements: 1, 3, 4, 5

4.   (b)

5.   false.

6.   false. Most economists would probably be content with describing "what is" or analyzing the consequences of "what could be," leaving "what ought to be" to politicians. A discussion of positive, normative and empirical economics may follow.

7.   matters pertaining to the economy as a whole (e.g.—recession, inflation, unemployment).

8.   particular aspects of the economy (e.g.—big business, labour unions, rent control)

9.   all skills, along with the ability to do mental work.

10.   it increases production per person (productivity), making higher living standards possible.

11.   productivity.

12.   (d)

13.   (d)

14.   the development of new technology—oil, natural gas or nuclear power.

15.   (a)

16.   (a)

17.   (c)

18.   (d)

19.   (e)

20.   opportunity cost

21.   (c)

22. effective, efficient

23. country II. The decision to produce more capital now increases their future production possibilities. Increasing capital improves labour productivity.

24. Susan's opportunity cost is $20 000.

25. (b) 52

    (c) 18

    (d) 10

    (e) underutilized, or misused

    (f) it would shift outward

    (g) increase

    (h) manual:

        $(4 \times 8 \times 15) + 70 + (10 \times 25) = \$800.$

        Per unit: $800 + 25 = \$32.$

        mechanized:

        $(2 \times 8 \times 15) + 70 + 290 + (10 \times 25) = \$850.$

        Per unit: $850 + 25 = \$34.$

    (i) manual:

        $(4 \times 8 \times 20) + 70 + (10 \times 25) = \$960.$

        Per unit: $960 + 25 = \$38.40.$

        mechanized:

        $(2 \times 8 \times 20) + 70 + (10 \times 25) + 290 = \$930.$

    (j) manual:

        $32 per unit.

        mechanized:

        $790 + 25 = \$31.60$ per unit.

    (k) manual:

        $32 per unit.

        mechanized:

        $900 + 25 = \$36$ per unit.

    (l) manual:

        $32 per unit.

mechanized:

(2 x 8 x 15) + 70 + (10 x 50) + 340 = $1150.

Per unit: 1150 ÷ 50 = $23.

(m) the type of technology used/productivity of capital.

26.

G	Economics
I	Inputs
M	Labour
L	Capital (equipment)
K	Productivity
H	Standard of living
J	Land
D	Output
A	Scarcity
B	Opportunity cost
C	Effectiveness
E	Efficiency
F	PPF

Chapter 2

1. consumers, as they make their spending decisions in the marketplace.

2. (d)

3. (d)

4. lowering the price of the product and the profits of the producers, thus reducing the incentive to produce that product.

5. producers, as they select the resource mix which will minimize production costs.

6. (a)

7. (e)

8. (d)

9. (a) true (e) false

   (b) true (f) false

(c)   false   (g)   false

(d)   true   (h)   true

10.   4 or 5 cents.

11.   (a)   payments to shareholders as dividends

(b)   to finance new investment in the business

12.   (a)   true   (c)   false

(b)   true   (d)   true

13.   (d)

14.   the government or government economic planners.

15.   inefficient use of resources; low quality of goods produced; inability to produce the goods that consumers want, resulting in shortages of some goods, surpluses of others.

16.   (1)   provide services to the public e.g. health care, education, law enforcement

(2)   regulate the operations and practices of business

(3)   redistribute income

17.   (b)

18.   (d)

19.   (a)   private   (b)   public municipal

(c)   private   (d)   public federal, provincial, municipal

(e)   public municipal   (f)   public municipal

(g)   private   (h)   public federal

(i)   public provincial   (j)   private

20.

D	Market system
F	Profits
B	Market power
C	Recessions
G	Command system
A	Subsidies
E	Gross Domestic Product (GDP)

Chapter 3

1.   (a)   yes   (c)   yes

    (b)   yes   (d)   yes

2.   (a)   It is easy to form.

    (b)   It provides strong incentives for the owner-manager.

3.   (a)   Once profits exceed a certain level, the sole proprietorship pays higher tax rates than payable on corporation profits.

    (b)   It does not have ready access to capital.

    (c)   It often lacks managerial expertise.

    (d)   Its owners have unlimited personal liability for the debts of the business.

4.   disagreements among the partners.

5.   (a)   The ability to raise large amounts of capital.

    (b)   The limited liability of its owners (shareholders).

    (c)   The lower tax rates on profits above a certain level (as compared to sole proprietorships and partnerships).

    (d)   The fact that a corporation is a separate legal entity from its shareholders, so that it continues to exist and function after the death of its owners.

6.   proprietorships and partnerships.

7.   (a)   no   (d)   no

    (b)   yes   (e)   no

    (c)   yes

8.   (a)

9.   (a)   true   (c)   false

    (b)   false   (d)   true

    (e)   true

10.   (d)

11.   (a)   financing problems,

    (b)   disproportionately heavy tax burden,

    (c)   government regulations and extensive paperwork,

    (d)   difficulties attracting and retaining capable employees.

12. an organization comprised of small businesses; lobby governments on behalf of small businesses.

13. corporations, raising large amounts of capital.

14. it represents a potential threat to Canada's markets by restricting competition, raising prices and reducing output (jobs).

15. (c)

16. shareholders; top management, Board of Directors; less; expertise.

17. a government owned and operated enterprise accountable to Parliament through a cabinet minister. As public policy tools they tend to perform functions the private sector would not or could not.

18. (a) false (c) true

    (b) false (d) true

19. (a) electrical generation and distribution,

    (b) transportation and communications,

    (c) energy and resources,

    (d) manufacturing.

20. Privatization is the process of selling off Crown corporations to the private sector, especially ones that are inefficient money losing enterprises.

21. They have contributed enormously to the economic development and unity of the nation. In such a large, widespread country as Canada, the costs of operating such enterprises are so great that it is necessary for the government to subsidize their operations in order to provide a reasonable level of service to Canadians.

22. They include money-losing businesses that the government acquired or maintained mainly for political reasons—mainly to "save jobs." Many government enterprises pay above-market wages and/or operate inefficiently, losing money regularly and falling back on the taxpayers for subsidies. These subsidies have contributed to past federal deficits.

23.

B	Sole proprietorship
E	Partnership
L	Limited partner
F	General partners
A	Corporation
D	Shareholders
M	Boards of Directors
G	Private corporation
C	Public corporation
H	Payroll taxes
I	Ebusinesses
N	Proxies
K	Crown corporations
J	Privatize

Chapter 4

1.   (d)

2.   falls.

3.   downward to the right.

4.   a specific amount that consumers are willing to purchase at a specific price.

5.

6. (a) decreases by 10 units.

    (b) remained the same.

7. (a) tastes and preferences: move in favor of the product.

    (b) income: increase.

    (c) price of substitutes: increase.

8. shift to the right (increase).

9. shift to the left (decrease).

10. shift to the left (decrease).

11. shift to the left (decrease).

12. shift to the left (decrease).

13. A product is inelastic (not sensitive to price changes) if

    (a) there are no close substitutes

    (b) it is a necessary good

14. price sensitive (or very sensitive to price changes).

15. (a) Ford Mustangs: many close substitutes available.

    (b) rye flour: substitutes are available.

    (c) long distance phone services: considered less necessary

16. (a) inelastic, it's the barbecue season, and there are not many close substitutes for barbecued steak.

    (b) elastic, the Canadian melons act as a substitute.

17. porterhouse steak, meat.

    there are many substitutes for a porterhouse steak, but few good substitutes for meat.

18. Total Revenue

        $500

        540

        560

        560

        540

    (a) inelastic   (c) unitary

    (b) inelastic   (d) elastic

19.   Revenue rises, but we must know how the costs are affected before we can determine whether or not the firm is better off.

20.   Insert (a)   2, elastic

          (b)   reduced, 7.5%

          (c) $37

21.   (c)

22.   0; 1.9; .5; infinite; .5; 2.8.

23.   larger

24.   elastic

25.

If Demand Is	The E Is	If Price	The TR Will
	0		decrease
	greater than 1 & less than ∞		increase
unitary elastic			remains constant
		increases	
perfectly elastic			increase/ decrease depending on the number of units sold

26.   You would not emphasize price since consumers are not particularly responsive to price considerations when demand is inelastic. Rather, you would emphasize factors such as the desirability or uniqueness of the product, its quality, design features, the image which the product bestows upon the owner.

27.   Price would be emphasized since consumers are responsive to price considerations. Retailers tend to stress prices in their advertising. Once the manufacturer's advertising has persuaded people to buy a particular product, the choice of retailers will depend largely on price.

28.   The strategy would backfire since the price increase would reduce the quantity demanded to such an extent that total sales revenue would decline, leaving the coffee producers worse off than before.

29.   The union's ability to raise wages (the price of labour) will largely depend upon the elasticity of demand for labour. Since the demand for plumbers is quite inelastic, there is much more scope for increasing their wages through union activity than there is for increasing the wages of hairdressers. The demand for

hairdressers' services is considerably more elastic, as there are substitutes and a greater ability to do without.

30.

D	Demand	
C	Elastic demand	
B	Inelastic demand	
A	Coefficient of elasticity	

Chapter 5

1. (c)

2. (a) many firms

   (b) freedom of entry and exit

3. (a)

4. (a) few firms

   (b) difficult to enter the industry

5. there is a lack of price competition.

6. (a) competitive   (e) competitive

   (b) concentrated   (f) concentrated

   (c) concentrated   (g) competitive

   (d) competitive

7. (c)

8. the quantity supplied increases.

9. (a) shift to the right (down).

   (b) lower production costs, more firms, better technology.

10. (a) shift to the left (up).

    (b) increased production costs, fewer firms, increased taxes.

11. decrease,

    to the left (up).

12.   increase,

        to the right (down).

13.   (a)   result in a relatively small change in the quantity supplied.

        (b)   Insufficient time to change the quantity supplied in response to a change in
                price; shortage of productive inputs.

14.   (a)   result in a relatively large change in the quantity supplied.

        (b)   Sufficient time for the producer to make changes in the quantity supplied;
                plentiful supply of productive inputs.

15.   More elastic.

        Given sufficient time, the producer can make major changes in the quantity
        supplied in response to a change in price.

16.   (a) $4   (d)   excess demand (35 units)

        (b)   25   (e)   1.5

        (c)   excess supply (15 units)

17.   (a)   increase   (d)   increase

        (b)   no change   (e)   increase

        (c)   increase

18.   (a)   Surplus of $10 billion.

        (b)   Shortage of $15 billion.

19.   (a)   3, 1, 2

        (b)   1, 3, 2

        (c)   3, 1, 2

        (d)   2, 3, 1

20.

        B   Market structure

        G   Competitive industry

        A   Market power

        L   Concentrated industries

        I   Price-maker

        C   Price-taker

        J   Supply schedule

D	Supply curve
E	Inelastic supply
K	Elastic supply
F	Equilibrium price
H	Equilibrium quantity

Chapter 6

1. increase; increase.

2. decrease; decrease.

3. decrease; increase.

4. increase; decrease.

5. (a)

6. (b)

7. (b)

8. (d)

9. The supply of people who could be president of a large company is much smaller than the supply of people who could work on an assembly line. The shortage of presidents of large companies drives up the wages that they receive.

10. No. The market clearing price in this market is indicated at 75 cents per unit. If producers charge $1.00 per unit, there will be unsold cauliflowers (excess supply). Since this is a perishable product, producers will have to lower their price back down towards the equilibrium level in order to sell off the existing quantity that was produced for this market.

11. Generally, the income position of the grain farmer has worsened rather than improved over the period in question.

Improved technology has resulted in greatly improved productivity and reduced manpower, as more efficient machinery has been introduced to the farming industry. The increased productivity has resulted in increasing supply of grain products. However, the industry supply curves remain relatively inelastic (particularly over the short term). This inelasticity, combined with increasing supply, has resulted in lower prices per unit. This decline in price is magnified when considering the market demand curve, which also is relatively inelastic. Thus, farm revenues have not increased significantly, while costs of production have had substantial increases (for fuel, fertilizers, insecticides, etc.). As a result, farm incomes have suffered.

12. (a) Increase in demand with supply constant, equilibrium price increases.

(b) Supply increases. With no change in demand, equilibrium price declines.

(c) Decrease in demand. Thus, prices decline.

13. $1.50

14. a surplus of 60 units (quantity supplied would be 80 units; quantity demanded would be 20 units).

15. a shortage of 40 units (quantity demanded would be 70 units; quantity supplied would be 30 units).

16. (a) increase in population will increase demand; price increases, quantity increases.

(b) Demand increases, supply does not since landlords are not motivated sufficiently to increase space and a shortage emerges if prices are unable to increase.

(c)

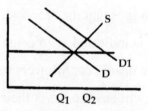

17. At a minimum wage of $7.00/hour, quantity of labour supplied will increase while the quantity of labour demanded will decrease. Quantity supplied will be greater than quantity demanded resulting in a surplus of labour (unemployment).

18.

D   Price support (floor)

A   Price control (ceiling)

B   Rent controls

E   Shortage

C   Surplus

Chapter 7

1.   many small firms, easy to enter the industry and all firms sell identical products.

2.   fall to zero

3.   (a)

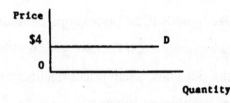

      (b)   (i)   Price remains at $4

             (ii)   Produce and sell as much as possible

      (c)   Improve efficiency by reducing per unit production costs

4.   (a)   (iv)   (it appears closest to perfect competition)

      (b)   many sellers,

             an identical product,

             each producer is small compared to the total industry output, each seller
             accepts the market price of $3.80.

      (c)

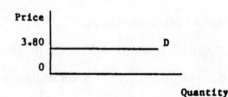

      (d)   Smith is not able to sell his product.

      (e)   No, Smith should not lower his price. He is able to sell all he can produce
             at the market price. Thus it is not necessary to lower the price since this
             only reduces profits.

      (f)   No, since he may sell as much as he wishes at the market price.

5.   (a)   many small firms

      (b)   easy to enter (and leave) the industry

6.   The products of all sellers are not identical—each producer's product is in some
      (relatively small) way different from the products of the others.

7.   (d)

8.   (e)

9.   (a)   (iii)

      (b)   inelastic

      (c)   Bob has created a "niche" market where his loyal customers are unlikely
             to buy more baked goods if the price drops. Similarly, the customers are
             willing to pay a higher price, if necessary with little if any reduction in
             quantities purchased. Thus, when prices decline, total revenues decline
             and when prices rise total revenues rise.

      (d)   his unique products, the Belgian pastries and birthday cakes.

10.   (f)

11.   (a)

12.   four; 50.

13.   (a)   oligopoly

      (b)   (i)   3 large firms accounting for 100% of sales;

             (ii)   each specializes to meet the demands of a unique segment of the
                     market;

             (iii)   little price competition since total sales decline for either price
                     increases or price decreases.

      (c)   No, because at $1650, quantity sold is 1.6 million tons. Thus, total
             revenues are $2.64 billion. This is $360 million less than the revenues
             derived at $1500 per ton. Regal's competitors have maintained the old
             price and captured 400 000 tons of Regal's business.

      (d)   No. A 10% reduction in price means $1350 per ton. Sales increases to 2.1
             million tons which means total revenues are $2.835 million. This is $165
             million less than the $3 billion derived at $1500 per ton.
             This time the steel competitors have reacted by lowering their price
             making for an inelastic demand schedule for Regal.

(e)   Price ($ per ton)

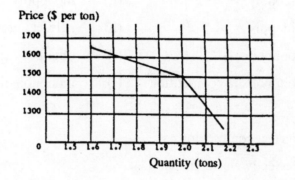

(f)   elastic, inelastic

14.   (a)   the amount of capital required

(b)   consumer acceptance/the cost of advertising

(c)   patents

(d)   government licences

(e)   predatory pricing by the established firms

(f)   mergers, in which established firms buy out newcomers

15.   (a)   false   (c)   false

(b)   true   (d)   false

16.   (d)

17.   supply

18.   (a)   yes   (d)   no

(b)   yes   (e)   yes

(c)   yes

19.   reducing prices; reducing output

20.   there is only one seller of a particular good or service with no close substitutes

21.   (e)

22.   (c)

23.   (a)   increase   (e)   increase

(b)   decrease   (f)   increase

(c)   decrease   (g)   increase

(d)   decrease

24.   (a)   monopoly   (f)   monopolistic competition

       (b)   oligopoly   (g)   monopoly

       (c)   oligopoly   (h)   perfect competition

       (d)   monopoly   (i)   oligopoly

       (e)   monopolistic competition   (j)   monopolistic competition

25.

       D   Perfect competition

       E   Perfectly elastic demand

       F   Monopolistic competition

       G   Product differentiation

       A   Oligopoly

       C   Monopoly

       I   Price-fixing

       B   Administered prices

       H   Price leadership

       L   Cartel

       J   Non-price competition

       K   Natural monopoly

Chapter 8

1.   (a)   fixed   (e)   fixed

       (b)   fixed   (f)   fixed

       (c)   variable   (g)   variable

       (d)   variable

2.   (c)

3.   (c)

4.   Law of Diminishing Returns

5.   (a)

6.   (a)   average fixed cost per unit due to the low volume of output

       (b)   average variable cost per unit is high due to the Law of Diminishing Returns

7.   (a)

8.   (c)

9.   (a)   20   (c)   15

         (b)   17

10.   (c)

11.   (b)

12.

Employment	Average Output
1	20
2	20
3	30
4	37.5
5	32

(a)   150 tables, 4 employees

(b)   fifth employee

(c)   variable

(d)

(2)	(3)	(4)	(5)	(6)
0	600	0	600	600/0 = infinity
20	600	1500	2100	2100/20 = 105
40	600	3000	3600	3600/40 = 90
90	600	4500	5100	5100/90 = 56.67
150	600	6000	6600	6600/150 = 44
160	600	7500	8100	8100/160 = 50.63

(e)

Tables/ Week	TR	TC	Profits
20	1100	2100	(1000)
40	2200	3600	(1400)
90	4950	5100	(150)
150	8250	6600	1650
160	8800	8100	700

(f)   150 tables, 4 employees, $1650 per week

(g)   Total losses exceeding total fixed costs which are both 20 and 40 tables in this example.

13.   (a)

Labour	Daily Output	Fixed Costs	Total Variable Costs	Total Cost	Average Total Cost	Marginal Cost	Total Revenues	Profits	Marginal Revenues
0	0	50	0	50	$—	—	—	—	—
1	1	50	80	130	130.00	80	75	(55)	75
2	3	50	180	230	76.67	50	225	(5)	75
3	7	50	320	370	52.86	35	525	155	75
4	9	50	420	470	52.22	50	675	205	75
5	10	50	500	550	55	80	750	200	75

13.   (a)

Labour	Daily Output	Fixed Costs	Total Variable Costs	Total Cost	Average Total Cost	Marginal Cost	Total Revenues	Profits	Marginal Revenues
0	0	50	0	50	$—	—	—	50	—
1	1	50	80	130	130.00	80	75	(55)	75
2	3	50	180	230	76.67	50	225	(5)	75
3	7	50	320	370	52.86	35	525	155	75
4	9	50	420	470	52.22	50	675	205	75
5	10	50	500	550	55	80	750	200	75

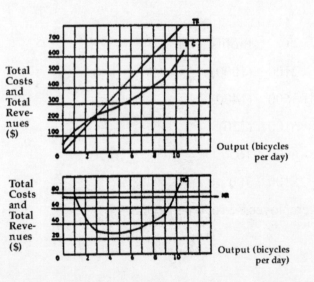

Total Costs and Total Revenues ($)   Output (bicycles per day)

Total Costs and Total Revenues ($)   Output (bicycles per day)

(b)   Hire 4 people and produce and sell 9 bicycles per day.

Profits are $205 per day.

(c)   According to the marginal cost/marginal revenue graph, the best profits

occur at between 9 and 10 bicycles per day as this is where MC=MR.

Since it is no use to produce part of a bicycle we must choose either 9 or

10 as the optimum output.

If the firm hires one more person and produces 10 bicycles, the

extra cost of this bicycle is $80, whereas the extra revenues derived from

the sale are only $75. Thus, they are reducing their existing profits by $5

(i.e., profits fall from $205 to $200 per day if 10 bicycles are

manufactured instead of 9).

(d)   Shut down since the table below indicates that losses exceed total fixed

costs at all levels of output.

Output	TR	TC	Profits
0	0	50	(50)
1	40	130	(90)
3	120	230	(110)
7	280	370	(90)
9	360	470	(110)
10	400	550	(150)

14.   (a)   310

(b) $2480

Method 1

Profits per unit:	$30 - $22 = $8
Total profits:	$8 x 310 = $2480

Method 2

Total revenues:	310 x $30 = $9300
Total costs:	$22 x 310 = $6820
Total profits:	$9300 - $6820 = $2480

(c)   Yes, because the demand curve is perfectly elastic. When extra profits are

apparent, new firms enter the industry. Price (AR on the graph) is pushed downward until the minimum ATC is reached. At this point ($20 on the graph) each firm makes only normal profits.

15. (a)

Units of Output Per Day	Fixed Costs	Variable Costs	Total Costs	Average Cost Per Unit	Average Revenue Per Unit	Marginal Cost Per Unit	Marginal Revenue Per Unit	Marginal Total Revenue
0	$300	$ 0	$ 300	—	—	—	—	—
300	300	850	1150	$3.38	$4.50	$2.83	$4.50	1350
600	300	1550	1850	3.08	4.00	2.33	3.50	2400
900	300	2050	2350	2.61	3.50	1.67	2.50	3150
1200	300	2500	2800	2.33	3.00	1.50	1.50	3600
1500	300	3100	3400	2.27	2.50	2.00	.50	3750
1800	300	4300	4600	2.56	2.00	4.00	(.50)	3600

(b)

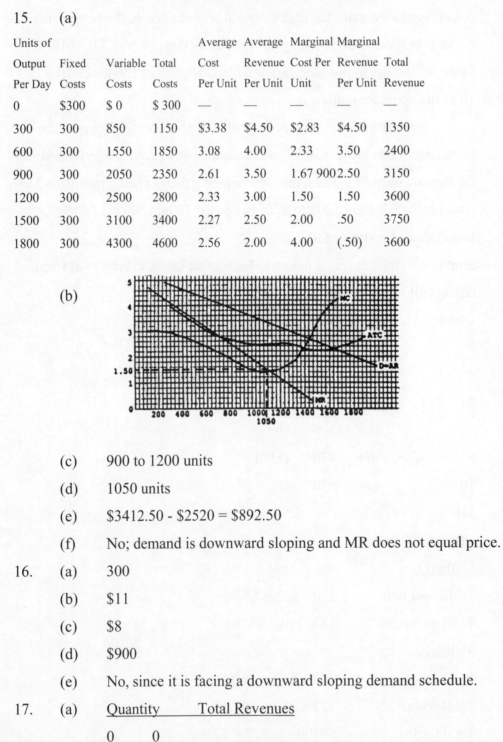

(c)   900 to 1200 units

(d)   1050 units

(e) $3412.50 - $2520 = $892.50

(f)   No; demand is downward sloping and MR does not equal price.

16. (a)   300

(b) $11

(c) $8

(d) $900

(e)   No, since it is facing a downward sloping demand schedule.

17. (a)

Quantity	Total Revenues
0	0
10	500
20	1000

30	1500
40	2000
50	2500

(b)

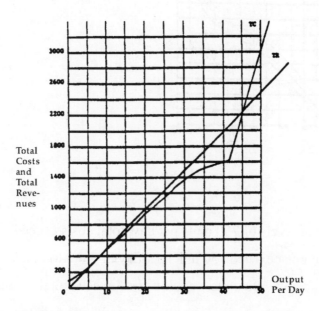

(c)   40 units

(d)   10; 10 and 46

(e) $100

18.   (a)

Units of Output

per Day	Fixed Costs	Variable Costs	Total Costs	Total Revenue
0	$300	$0	$ 300	$ 0
200	300	900	1200	700
400	300	1600	1900	1400
600	300	2100	2400	2100
800	300	2400	2700	2800
1000	300	3100	3400	3500
1200	300	4300	4600	4200

(b)

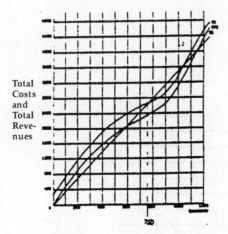

Total
Costs
and
Total
Reve-
nues

750

(c)   750

(d)   600

Below output levels of 750 units per day, total costs exceed total revenue; thus, output must exceed 750 units per day in order to break even. If output falls below 600 units, variable costs exceed total revenue, so that it would be less costly to close the business and have only the fixed costs to pay.

19.

D	Fixed costs
B	Variable costs
E	Law of Diminishing Returns
F	Marginal productivity (per worker)
B	Marginal cost per unit
C	Marginal revenue per unit

Chapter 9

1.   (a)   Gaining economies of scale

      (b)   Improving access to financial resources

      (c)   Strengthening marketing networks

2.   (b)

3.   (e)

4.   true

5.   (a)   yes   (d)   yes

      (b)   yes   (e)   yes

      (c)   no

6.   (a)   attractive tax incentives

      (b)   weak Canadian legislation prohibiting mergers and takeovers

      (c)   a desire on the part of corporate management to beat out rumoured changes in federal law.

7.   higher, lower, lower

8.   (c)

9.   (a)   no   (d)   no

      (b)   yes   (e)   no

      (c)   no   (f)   yes

10.   competitive, oligopolistic.

11.   In sum, there is a tendency towards industrial concentration which restricts supply and raises prices and profits.

      Price competition is replaced by advertising, superficial product differentiation and price-fixing.

      The appropriate government policy called for is legislation aimed at preventing price-fixing and mergers and the formulation of any other measures that would reduce competition.

12.   (a)   no   (f)   yes

      (b)   no   (g)   yes

      (c)   yes   (h)   no

      (d)   no   (i)   yes

      (e)   yes

13.   (a)   true   (d)   false

      (b)   false   (e)   false

      (c)   false

14.   (a)   elasticity of demand (especially due to foreign competition);

      (b)   lack of cooperation among oligopolists;

      (c)   fear of government action, as price-fixing is illegal;

(d)   desire for growth;

(e)   desire for a good public image;

(f)   countervailing power.

15.   In general terms, a representative of big business would probably argue that big is not so bad. He may suggest that big business has benefited consumers, that criticisms are unfounded and inaccurate, that the power of big business is exaggerated and subject to limitations and that it is a source of significant economic benefits to the economy.

16.   less; less protected against oligopolistic practices.

17.   Royal Bank of Canada, Bank of Montreal, disallowed.

18.   increase

       decrease

       increase

       decrease

       increase

       decrease

19.   (e)

20.   On average, Canadian top firms are smaller than their foreign counterparts. Industrial concentration in Canada is higher than comparable industries in the USA. In other words, Canadian firms large enough to threaten Canadian consumers are weak competitors internationally. Legislation aimed at restricting growth and concentration domestically to protect consumers could also prohibit Canadian firms from growing large enough to be internationally competitive. This in turn can threaten employment in Canada's already weak manufacturing sector. Policy makers are damned if they do and if they don't.

21.   (d)

22.   (a)   no   (d)   no

       (b)   yes   (e)   yes

       (c)   no   (f)   yes

23.   (c)

24. promote development of Canadian manufacturing industries through tariffs, which protect Canadian manufacturers against foreign competition.

25. more intense, Japan and Southeast Asia.

26. the Canada-USA Free Trade Agreement, 1989.

27. efficiency gains, compete internationally

28. a price-fixing conspiracy; a large-scale merger.

29.

D	Laissez-faire
F	Marketing boards
G	Industrial concentration
A	Economies of scale
B	Globalization
C	Merger
E	Price-fixing

Chapter 10

1. supply and demand for each particular job skill.

2. $6

3. $7

4. an excess supply of 6000 workers.

5. False: the more inelastic the supply, the steeper is the supply curve, and there will be a greater impact in the market given any change in demand.

6. Workers often face obstacles in attempting to move to the higher paying jobs. Sometimes they lack the skills and abilities that are required, and in other cases they have not had the opportunity to aquire the necessary education. For some high paying jobs, such as those performed by entertainers or professional athletes, few workers have the necessary talents. Therefore, the wage differentials persist, as the scarcity of labour continues for the high paying jobs.

7. It creates imbalance (disequilibrium) in the market resulting in an excess supply (surplus) of labour at the artificially high price. The more elastic the demand the greater the surplus.

Therefore, job loss depends on the demand elasticities in the industries involved. For example: in tourism, the largest of minimum wage employers, demand is inelastic. People want personal service; despite increases in the minimum wage, hotel and restaurant business has increased. As long as **all** employers must pay the additional costs, the bulk of it can be passed on to the consumer. But if the product demand is elastic, any attempt by the employer to pass on higher wage costs will cause a loss of business, resulting in less employment.

8. Governments may legislate minimum wage laws in an attempt to increase the incomes of low-wage earners, and thereby create more equity in the labour market. It may be argued that increases in the minimum wage rate do not necessarily result in layoffs of employees, although they might discourage the hiring of new employees. For those workers who are able to keep their jobs, the higher minimum wage rate will certainly improve their economic well-being.

9. 26%

10. 28%, 35%

11. (a) yes   (d) yes
    (b) yes   (e) yes
    (c) no   (f) no

12. the individual workers

13. file a grievance against the employer.

14. (b)

15. (a) false (d) false
    (b) true   (e) true
    (c) false

16. 95%

17. less than one-eighth of one percent

18. (d)

19. (b)

20. (d)

21.   Contract negotiations take place as usual, including conciliation, but if no agreement is reached, the dispute goes to arbitration for a final decision.

22.   (1)   decrease in number of work stoppages

      (2)   decrease in time lost due to work stoppages

      (3)   union-management cooperative efforts regarding worker training, and improvements to productivity and product quality.

23.   the increasing degree of international competition in industry and the need for Canadian industry to be internationally competitive.

24.

      E   Derived demand

      H   Short run

      B   Long run

      I   Minimum wage

      A   Individual bargaining

      C   Collective bargaining

      D   Collective agreement

      J   Compulsory conciliation

      F   Grievance

      G   Arbitration

Chapter 11

1.   (a), (b), (d), (e)

2.   (a)   shifts in consumer demand, which have placed increasing emphasis on services

      (b)   changes in production technology, which have altered industry's labour requirements

3.   (c)

4.   (a)

5.   (a)   yes   (d)   no

      (b)   no   (e)   no

      (c)   yes   (f)   yes

6.   (a)   rising productivity creates higher living standards, which increase demand for goods, thus creating jobs

       (b)   rising productivity allows Canadian business to compete more effectively in foreign markets, thus creating additional jobs

7.   (a)   True   (c)   False

       (b)   True   (d)   False

8.   (e)

9.   slower productivity growth; decrease in the growth of income earners per family.

10.   41.5%, 6.3%%

11.   72%

12.   differences in hours worked; training, education, experience

13.   occupational segregation

14.   (a)   (1) clerical (2) service (3) sales (4)medicine/health care (5) teaching

       (b)   These occupational groupings contain many relatively low paying jobs. The large number of women employed in these areas causes the average wage paid to women to be lower.

15.   The value of work can be measured according to a point system, which accounts for such factors as skill, effort, responsibility and working conditions. The points awarded for one particular job can be compared with points awarded for a different job, even in a different profession. If the points awarded for two jobs are equal, then the values of the two jobs are deemed to be equal.

16.   (d)

17.   5.1 million

18.   Critics allege that LICO's is more a measure of income inequality, rather than a measure of poverty. It indicates that people whose incomes are far enough below average are to be classified as poor. The use of LICO's guarantees that the levels of poverty will always be nearly at the same level, even when general income levels are rising.

19.   MBM poverty lines differ from LICO's in that they do not measure the poverty line as being below a certain percentage of average income. Instead, they conclude a family to be poor if they are unable to afford the necessities of life.

20.   (a)   nutritious meals as defined by Health Canada

      (b)   clothing for work and social occasions

      (c)   a median cost three bedroom apartment

      (d)   other necessary items such as personal care, household needs, furniture, telephone service, etc.

21.   (c)

22.   single parent mothers

23.   E   Poverty line

      C   Low income cut-off

      H   Market basket measure

      J   National Council of Welfare

      D   Poverty rate

      B   Equal pay for work of equal value

      A   Income distribution

      I   Physical definition of poverty (Note: also called "absolute" definition)

      K   Labour force participation rate

      G   Transfer payment

      F   Relative (social) definition of poverty

Chapter 12

1.   increase, 21%, nearly 52%, 40%. crown

2.   providing public services, redistributing income, regulating actions.

3.   the imposition of constraints backed by government authority, that are intended to modify the economic behaviour of individuals in the private sector significantly.

4.   (a)   income security

      (b)   health care

      (c)   education

5.   (d)

6.   (b)

7.   (a)   Brought in Unemployment Insurance Program in 1942.

       (b)   Canadian Pension, 1956.

       (c)   Child Tax Credit, 1978.

       (d)   Guaranteed Income Supplement, 1966.

       (e)   Hospital insurance and medicare programs were introduced.

       (f)   Indexing numerous welfare programs to keep pace with the CPI.

       (g)   Increasing inflation and unemployment.

       (h)   Increase in the number of tax expenditures.

8.   income security

9.   to reduce the tax burden on low income Canadians.

10.   (a)   false   (d)   true

       (b)   false   (e)   false

       (c)   false   (f)   true

11.   30%

12.   (d)

13.   False. The tax system is not nearly as progressive as is generally believed and is regressive for very low income people.

14.   Goods and Services Tax

15.   incomes, consumption, spending, assets

16.   lower, regressive

17.   Advantages

    –major source of tax revenue for government

    –may be applied at the manufacturer's level and be invisible at the retail level

    –can assist in deficit reduction

    Disadvantages

    –may be economically damaging to the nation

    –may become a discriminatory tax

    –may favour imports over domestically produced goods

18.   to replace the Federal Sales Tax on manufactured goods with a more broadly-based consumption (sales) tax on a wide range of goods and services.

19.

Seller	Buyer	Price	Tax	Rebate	Net Tax
Iron Ore Producer	Steel Producer	$1 000	$70	$0	$70
Steel Producer	Car Manufacturer	$5 000	$350	$70	$280
Car Manufacturer	Car Dealer	$10 000	$700	$350	$350
Car Dealer	Consumer	$16 000	$1 200	$700	$500

Note: the total in the Net Tax column is $1 200 (the amount paid by the consumer)

20.   incentives to invest and expand

21.   (a)   too complex and inefficient

       (b)   inequitable

       (c)   generates disincentives or negative externalities

       (d)   ineffective

22.   all statements are true

23.   (e)

24.   When all taxes are considered, the tax system does not redistribute income in the
       progressive way that is generally presumed. However, when government
       spending is considered, the net effect of government is to redistribute income
       from the upper-income third of families towards the others, especially the lowest-
       income third. On the other hand, the net effect of government programs is not as
       progressive as is generally believed beyond quite low income levels.

25.   (a)   they contribute to rising interest rates;

       (b)   they depress business investment spending;

       (c)   they threaten to undermine Canada's social welfare system;

       (d)   the interest payments on them are increasingly taking a larger portion of
              the government's budget.

26.   (a)   true   (d)   true

       (b)   true   (e)   true

       (c)   true

27.   fierce political resistance.

28.   50

29.   Transfer payments to the provinces for health care, post-secondary education and welfare.

30.   False: If all the income in 1981 in excess of $39 999 were redistributed to taxpayers with incomes of less than $40 000, each would have received $385.59. Besides, a few years of economic growth would do more for the poor.

31.   Students should be directed to put forth economic arguments and reserve their political comments until they have explored Chapter 13.

32.   reduce debt, increase spending, reduce taxes.

33.   Programs funded by the federal government use economic resources. Thus, funding for the military directs resources into the military and not into health care or into some other endeavor. Thus, if taxes are not increased, the opportunity cost of increasing the military budget could be a loss of services for health care or for some other program. If taxes are raised to fund the military, money will be transferred from private hands leaving fewer consumer goods available to the public.

34.   C   Gross domestic product

        J   Tax credit

        K   Consumption tax

        B   Progressive tax

        D   Marginal tax rate

        L   Regressive tax

        G   Payroll tax

        F   Budget deficit

        H   User fees

        A   Federal debt

        E   Regulation

        M   Fiscal

        I   Budget surplus

Chapter 13

1. (a)   free enterprise

    (b)   the market system;

    (c)   individual responsibility for one's own economic fate.

2. the operation of free markets.

3. profit.

4. powerful and wealthy.

5. rich and powerful.

6. an active role for government in the economy.

7. left

8. right

9. left

10. incentives for people to save and invest their capital in business enterprises, which provide employment and prosperity.

11. right

12. do not

13. taxes and transfer payments.

14. left; they see unions as organizations of workers to protect themselves against exploitation by employers.

15. exploitation by employers.

16. socialism

17. right

18. raise, discourages, slows.

19. (a)   unequal distribution of income

    (b)   social instability

    (c)   economic instability

20. (a)   less incentive to work, save, invest

    (b)   higher interest rates

    (c)   a decrease in productivity

21. left

22. right

23.   budget deficits, incentives for businesses to invest and provide more jobs.

24.   (d)

25.   In an effort to reduce costs and improve the level of services, some right wingers have recommended that selected health care services be privatized, or at least that private suppliers of health care be allowed to offer their services, along with government operated providers. Left wingers have objected to any intrusion of private health care providers into the health care system. They suggest that the introduction of private enterprise into the public health care system will lead to a "two-tier" health system—one for the rich and another for the poor.

26.   D   Efficiency

       B   Income distribution

       A   Capitalism

       E   Philosophy

       C   Principle

Chapter 14

1.   better economic times, serious environmental problems.

2.   Private costs are costs paid by producers and included in the price paid by the consumer.
      Social costs are costs paid by society at large and not included in the price paid by the consumer.

3.   (c)

4.   minimize

5.   An externality is an incidental cost or benefit derived from a product or service, e.g., goodwill.

6.   (a)   yes   (d)   yes
      (b)   yes   (e)   no
      (c)   yes

7.   (d)

8.   (a)

9.   the objective of pollution control targets

      how to protect the environment

      who should pay for abatement

10.   (a)   false   (c)   true

      (b)   true   (d)   false

11.   acid rain; greenhouse effect; depletion of the ozone layer

12.   (c)

13.   (a)   difficult to set a limit for pollution.

      (b)   difficult to measure the external costs, therefore a problem in establishing

             the appropriate tax.

      (c)   complexity of law suits, long time period required for a judgement.

      (d)   this policy may make pollution socially acceptable.

14.   may be appropriate if the cost of installing pollution control equipment is so high

      that it could force the firm to close, with a resulting loss of jobs.

15.   (a)

16.   (a)   no   (d)   yes

      (b)   no   (e)   yes

      (c)   yes   (f)   yes

17.   illegal dumping, compacting garbage in order to increase the amount placed in

      each container.

18.   carbon dioxide, fossil fuels, automobile. Reduce energy consumption, accept

      lower economic growth and lower standards of living.

19.   The public is more concerned with environmental problems during the boom

      period of the economic cycle. When the economy is in recession and jobs are

      scarce, in the interests of reducing the levels of unemployment, the public is less

      likely to object to economic initiatives that may be harmful to the environment.

      During good economic times the public believes that an opportunity exists for

      industry to clean up its operations, and households may be motivated to do the

      same. The cost of doing so is more affordable when unemployment is at low

      levels.

20.	E	Private (internal) cost
	D	Social (external) cost
	B	Diminishing returns
	C	Kyoto protocol
	F	Greenhouse effect
	A	Pollution
	G	Economic tradeoff

Chapter 15

1. (b)

2. (a)

3. (e)

4. (b)

5. (c)

6. (a) no (d) yes

    (b) yes (e) yes

    (c) no

7. (b)

8. $8 to $4, fall, rise.

9. (a)

10. less

11. a surplus of 60 (quantity supplied=100, quantity demanded=40).

12. paid farmers not to grow some crops.

13. (a) no (d) no

    (b) yes (e) no

    (c) no

14. 100; $2

15. pay the farmers a subsidy of $6 for each unit sold at the market price of $2, to bring the price received by farmers up to the target price of $8.

16. (d)

17. restrict the output and increase the prices of farm products.

18.   (a)   no   (d)   yes

      (b)   yes   (e)   yes

      (c)   yes

19.   (a)   yes   (c)   yes

      (b)   yes   (d)   no

20.

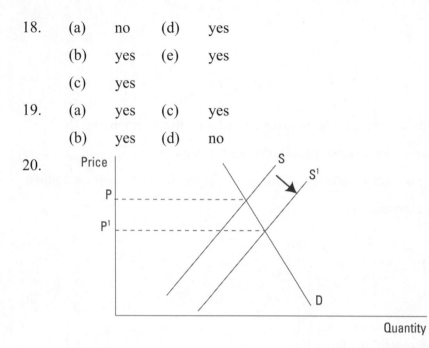

Subsidies paid to European and American grain producers encourage producers to produce larger volumes of grain than they would grow if there were no subsidy payments. This results in an increase in world grain supplies, shown by a rightward shift in the supply curve, to position S^1. The market equilibrium price drops from its former level P to P^1. Since most of Canada's grain output is exported, producers have no choice but to accept the world market price, which may be so low that they are unable to cover their production costs, causing them to be in a loss position.

21   (c), because this approach does not reduce the volume of food produced nor does it discourage improved efficiency.

22.   B   Agricultural revolution

      G   "Farm problem"

      H   "Offer to Purchase"

      A   "Acreage restriction" crop management program

      C   "Deficiency payment" farm support program

      I   Agricultural marketing board

      E   World Trade Organization

      D   Productivity

      F   Subsidy

Chapter 16

1. (e)

2. lower tariff barriers, increase in the number of trading nations, improved computer, communications and transportation technology.

3. inefficiency of our industry, putting Canada at a competitive disadvantage against increased foreign competition.

4. (d)

5. (a)   6   (d)   8
    (b)   2   (e)   3, 7
    (c)   1, 4   (f)   5

6. B   "Resource wealth mentality"
    A   Deregulation
    C   Efficiency
    G   Productivity
    F   Privatization
    E   Subsidy
    D   Crown corporation

Macro Chapter 1

WHAT IS ECONOMICS?

This chapter deals with introductory matters such as the definition of economics and the nature of the subject, which ranges from technical analysis to value judgments, to broad philosophical issues. Economics involves a way of thinking about our worldly whims and woes. For example, should the government regulate electricity rates, gasoline prices or car insurance rates to halt rising prices? Has our welfare state made us lazy? In economics we approach these issues by examining how they bear on our motivations as buyers and on our incentives as producers. While such analysis does not automatically determine the right answers, it clarifies the economic consequences of our choices before we act on them. We support questions first and actions later.

For purposes of studying economics, the subject is divided into two sections: macroeconomics, which deals with the overall operation of the economy, and microeconomics, which focuses on particular aspects of the economic system.

General Learning Objective

Consider the scope, the purpose, and the approaches to the study of economics.

Specific Learning Objectives

		Self-Test Reference
1.	Develop a definition of economics.	#1-2
2.	Distinguish between effectiveness and efficiency .	#3
3.	Consider the limitations of economic analysis .	#4-6
4.	Identify the three types of resources and their characteristics.	#7-12
5.	Recognize the "economic problem."	#13-15

Self-Test

1.   "Economics," as the term is used in its broadest sense, deals with

     (a)   decisions made by society concerning the production of goods.

     (b)   decisions made by society concerning the distribution of goods.

     (c)   how a society satisfies the material needs and wants of its people.

     (d)   all of the above.

2.   Economics (is/is not) a precise science like mathematics because _____

     _____

     _____

3.   Which statement concerning effectiveness and efficiency is correct?

     (a)   An effective supplier of goods and services reduces costs, but an efficient supplier focuses on producing goods and services that are needed.

     (b)   An effective supplier focuses on what is profitable and an efficient supplier focuses on what is in demand.

     (c)   An effective supplier focuses on goods and services that are most valued, and an efficient supplier finds ways to reduce costs.

     (d)   One can not be both effective and efficient, since effectiveness can only be achieved at the expense of efficiency.

4.   Which is correct? Economic analysis of a policy issue:

     (a)   will provide the government with a decision as to which policy choice is best.

     (b)   will help to clarify the economic consequences of various policies and improve the basis for decision making.

5.   TRUE or FALSE? The disagreement which is so common among economists shows that the field of economics is so inconclusive and contradictory that the analysis and recommendations of economists cannot be taken seriously.

_____

_____

6.   TRUE or FALSE? The study of economics emphasizes "what ought to be" rather than "what is" or "what could be." Explain.

_____

_____

7.   Besides the physical ability to do work, the labour input includes _____

_____

8.   Capital equipment is particularly important because _____

_____

_____

9.   Increases in "output per worker" are defined as increases in _____.

10.   The land resource includes

       (a)   any product manufactured from a natural element such as iron.

       (b)   forests, fields and streams.

       (c)   energy sources provided by nature.

       (d)   (b) and (c) above.

11.   In a "resource rich" country such as Canada

       (a)   land provides such an unlimited supply of materials that it could not be described as "scarce."

       (b)   labour is abundant, rather than scarce, as is demonstrated by the high unemployment figures.

       (c)   capital is the most abundant of all three resources.

       (d)   all resources would still be described by economists as being "scarce."

12.   While some of the earth's resources become depleted, other resources are being created through _____. One example is _____.

13.   Basic human needs (i.e., those material things necessary to sustain life) are

    (a)   limited.   (c)   abundant.

    (b)   infinite.   (d)   scarce.

14.   Human wants are

    (a)   endless, since people everywhere appear to desire more goods than are available.

    (b)   limited, due to the finite nature of resources.

    (c)   always short of what society is capable of producing.

    (d)   proportionate to human needs.

15.   The economic problem facing any society would be less serious if

    (a)   human wants were limited.

    (b)   resources were more abundant.

    (c)   technology advanced at a more rapid pace.

    (d)   all of the above.

16.   The choice made by politicians to spend on hospital construction instead of helicopters is an example of the concept of _____

17.   The "what" problem in economics means that

    (a)   goods and services should be produced as efficiently as possible.

    (b)   economists have a responsibility to tell us what goods to produce.

    (c)   every society should produce only those goods which it can produce most efficiently.

    (d)   government must direct our productive efforts.

    (e)   every society must in some way decide what goods it will produce (and not produce).

18.   "How to produce" would not be a problem for society if

    (a)   technology were to improve in all areas.

    (b)   natural resources were in no danger of being depleted.

    (c)   only one mix of inputs were possible in the production of any product.

    (d)   all resources were equally scarce.

19. Bob Shaftoe, a small regional retailer, wanted to expand his business interests, so he decided to acquire a manufacturing enterprise from one of his local suppliers. He reasoned that if he could fully employ the business' existing resources he would be able to produce one or a combination of two products for his customers according to the table found on p. 6 of this study guide.

Upon further investigation, Bob determined that the business could produce product B using either of two production methods: manual or mechanical. Manual production requires 4 employees, working 8 hours per day at $15 per hour. Mechanized production requires only 2 employees and processing equipment which costs $290 per day to operate. Either method will produce 25 units of product B per day. Overhead costs for each method are $70 per day, and material costs are $10 per unit of output.

(a)   According to the above figures, the (manual/mechanized) production method is the most efficient.

(b)   If wage rates increased by $5 per hour, then the (manual/mechanized) production method would be most efficient.

(c)   If wage rates remained at $15 per hour and processing equipment costs declined by $60 per day, then the (manual/mechanized) production method would be most efficient.

(d)   If processing equipment costs increased to $340 per day, then the (manual/mechanized) production method would be most efficient.

(e)   If new processing equipment were purchased that doubled output and increased operating costs by $50 per day, then the (manual/mechanized) production method would be most efficient.

20. In a market system, decisions regarding what to produce are made for the most part by _____

21.   The interaction between buyers and sellers in the market for "bananas" results in the establishment of:

    (a)   prices of bananas but not the quantity traded.

    (b)   the quantity of bananas traded, but not the price.

    (c)   neither price nor quantity of bananas being traded.

    (d)   both prices and quantity of bananas being traded.

22.   The market type of economic system would correct a shortage of a product by:

    (a)   lowering the price of the product and the profits of the business firms causing the shortage.

    (b)   lowering the price of the product but increasing profits and output of the product by means of a government subsidy.

    (c)   government instructions to producers to increase production of the product.

    (d)   raising the price of the product and the profits of its producers.

    (e)   doing none of the above.

23.   A market system type of economy would correct a surplus (oversupply) of a product by _____

_____

24.   In a market type of economic system, the questions of what to produce, how to produce it, and for whom to produce are basically decided by

    (a)   the government.

    (b)   tradition.

    (c)   the people, working consciously for the social good rather than for their own interests.

    (d)   the free decisions of households and businesses, made out of self-interest.

    (e)   economists.

25.   Which of the following statements regarding the market system type of economy are **TRUE**, and which are **FALSE**?

    _____ (a)   It is a consumer-oriented production system.

    _____ (b)   It provides strong work incentives for people.

_____ (c)   It grows steadily, and is not prone to economic fluctuations and crises, such as recessions or depressions.

_____ (d)   It tends to generate a high material standard of living.

_____ (e)   It tends to result in an equal distribution of economic benefits among various groups and individuals.

_____ (f)   Its production methods tend to be less efficient than those of other systems.

_____ (g)   Private economic power groups are unable to become established and enrich themselves at the expense of less powerful groups.

26.   If Beverly owns $12 000 of stock of Consolidated Freebles Ltd., and receives annual dividends of $720, the "rate of return" on her investment (before tax) is _____%.

27.   State whether each of the following statements regarding business profits is **TRUE** or **FALSE**.

_____ (a)   They provide strong incentives for businesses to produce what the consumers want.

_____ (b)   They provide strong incentives for businesses to produce goods and services as efficiently as possible.

_____ (c)   They are considerably larger than the general public supposes them to be.

_____ (d)   They are an important source of funds for capital investment, which increases prosperity.

28.   Mary Jones invested $60 000 of her savings in her own word processing business. The business attained sales of $100 000 in the first year of operation and total costs came to $95 000. Thus, Mary was left with $5000. Of the $5000, $1250 was paid in taxes on profits, $2750 was spent on new word processing software, and Mary put aside $1000 for her personal use.

Determine:

(a)   Profits (before tax) _____.

(b)   Profits (after tax) _____.

(c)   Mary's before-tax rate of return on her investment is _____.

(d)   The profits are composed of (fill in the blanks)

Taxes + New Investment + Payments to Owners = Total Profit

_____ + _____ + _____ = _____

(e)   Suppose that in addition to the $5000 profit earned by the business Mary also paid herself a salary of $30 000 but in her first year in business turned down a salaried position for $35 000.

29.   List three areas in which government gets involved in economic decision making in a mixed economy such as Canada's:

1.   _____

      _____

2.   _____

      _____

3.   _____

      _____

30. Match the definitions on the right with the terms on the left.

	Economic resources	A	Providing the goods and services most valued by society.
	Economic input	B	A situation in which some resources in the economy are not being used.
	Labour	C	A measure of the total value of the goods and services produced in an economy.
	Capital Equipment	D	A payment by government to a producer for the purpose of reducing the production cost.
	Return on investment	E	Profit earned divided by the financial contribution of the owner.
	Living standard	F	Both the public and private sectors are significantly involved in the production of goods and services.
	Land	G	Tools, buildings and equipment used in the production of goods and services.
	Output	H	An economic resource.
	Scarcity	I	The goods and services produced from the economic inputs.
	Opportunity cost	J	Refers to how income is divided between wealthy, middle and poor people in the country.
	Effectiveness	K	The skills and talents that people use to make a living.

	Efficiency	L	The difference between revenues and expenses.
	Market system	M	A reflection of society's prosperity measured in terms of goods and services consumed.
	Profit	N	Economic decisions are made by consumers and privately owned producers.
	Market power	O	Labour, capital equipment and natural resources used to produce goods and services.
	Recession	P	The wanting of goods and services exceeds the means of producing them.
	Subsidy	Q	Any natural resource available as an economic input.
	Gross domestic product	R	Using resources in a way that makes the cost as cheap as possible.
	Income distribution	S	The ability of a seller to raise the price.
	Mixed economic system	T	The real cost of producing something or satisfying a want, which is the foregone opportunity of not producing something else.

Macro Chapter 2

INTRODUCTION TO MACROECONOMICS

The transition from micro to macroeconomics can be compared to a shift in our eye's focus — from the observance of a very close object which we see in great detail to the observance of a number of more distant objects which we contemplate as a group. For example, in a microeconomics context, we may very well observe how a particular oil company is adjusting the price of its gasoline at the pump over the change of several seasons. In macroeconomics, our focus would more likely be on the movement of price levels of thousands of finished goods throughout the entire economy.

The macro dimension may at first appear to be on so large a scale that its study would be beyond the realm of introductory economics. Indeed, there are a number of very complex problems that face any nation's macro economy, but it may be reassuring for you to realize that we use the same basic tools in its study as we used in microeconomics: supply, demand, and their interaction.

Since a study of macroeconomics involves statistics relating to our total performance, it is important for economists to be able to measure the various economic aggregates in order to compare actual performance with our stated goals. Three measuring rods that are used extensively in macroeconomic analysis are introduced in this chapter: Gross Domestic Product, the unemployment rate, and the Consumer Price Index (which in turn is related to the rate of inflation).

Many of the measurements used to determine the Gross Domestic Product, unemployment, and the inflation rate are obtained by estimates and various sampling techniques. While the resulting statistics do not necessarily represent precise values, they do provide a basis for useful comparisons with previous periods, provided that the techniques used are consistent.

General Learning Objectives

Establish the basic framework for the study of macroeconomics.

Assess Canada's economic performance, using statistics relating to the Gross Domestic Product, unemployment, the Consumer Price Index, and the rate of inflation.

Specific Learning Objectives

Self-Test

1. Which of the following reflect a macroeconomic issue, and which involve microeconomics?

    _____ (a)   The average number of shares traded on the Toronto Stock Exchange over a five-day period.

_____ (b)   The interest rate offered by General Motors on a new bond issue.

_____ (c)   The need to restructure Canada's industry as a result of expanded world trade patterns.

_____ (d)   Canada's merchandise trade balance.

_____ (e)   The improvement in farm productivity over the past two decades.

_____ (f)   The current unemployment rate in Canada.

2.   Explain how each of the following factors would influence the "supply side" of a nation's economy:

(a)   skill levels of its labour force

_____

_____

_____

(b)   quantity and quality of its capital equipment

_____

_____

_____

(c)   the profit motive

_____

_____

_____

3.   The four groups of buyers that account for total spending in an economy are represented by

(a)   consumers, business, governments, and farm producers.

(b)   consumers, exporters, importers, and corporations.

(c)   consumers, business, exporters, and government.

(d)   consumers, business, governments, and foreign buyers.

4.   Total spending on goods and services is known as a nation's _____.

5.   The consequence for the economy of demand being low relative to supply is

(a)   an economic boom.

(b)   inflation.

(c)   unemployment.

(d)   recession.

(e)   (c) and (d) above.

6.   If an economy is functioning properly, how would you describe the level of each
       of the following:

       (a)   output of goods and services _____

               _____

       (b)   employment _____

               _____

       (c)   inflation _____

               _____

7.   Gross/Domestic Product (GDP) is defined as _____

       _____

       _____

8.   The four major components of GDP are

       (a)   _____

       (b)   _____

       (c)   _____

       (d)   _____

9.   Match the major components of GDP with the following statements.

       _____ (a)   The Government of Canada builds a new technology centre.

       _____ (b)   A Canadian family take a summer vacation to Wally World, USA.

       _____ (c)   An entrepreneur purchases new equipment for a business.

       _____ (d)   Americans buy cedar shingles from British Columbia.

       _____ (e)   Canada Construction builds 100 homes for sale to senior citizens.

       _____ (f)   A student purchases a computer to assist her in her studies.

       _____ (g)   An American executive attends a convention in Halifax.

       _____ (h)   A retailer orders next fall's inventory.

10.   Iron ore is sold to a steel mill for $80 000 to be made into steel. That steel is sold
       to a metal fabricating plant for $180 000, and is made into filing cabinets that are
       sold for $260 000. The actual addition to GDP arising from these transactions by
       using the expenditure approach is $_____.

11. If consumption spending is $100 billion, investment spending is $40 billion, government spending is $60 billion, exports are $80 billion, and imports are $60 billion, GDP will be $ _____ billion.

12. If GDP = 430, C = 200, G = 150, I = 60, X = 50; then M = _____.

13. Total incomes generated from the spending components in Question 12 will amount to $_____.

14. Money GDP (current GDP) is calculated in terms of

_____.

15. Real GDP (constant dollar GDP) differs from the above definition in that real

GDP _____.

16. Historically, money GDP has risen faster than real GDP because

_____

17. Three things not measured by GDP are _____,

_____ and _____.

18. (a) If Statistics Canada reports that Canada's Gross Domestic Product was $848 billion in 1997, what does this statistic *mean*?

    (b) If the GDP had been $800 billion in 1996, the 1997 figure of $848 billion would represent a 6% increase over 1996. Does this mean that Canada's economy produced 6% *more output* in 1997 than in 1996?

19.

Year	Money GDP (billions)	Real GDP (billions)	GDP Deflator
1991	478	489	(1)—
1992	506	(2)—	100.0
1993	552	526	104.9
1994	606	553	(3)—
1995	651	566	115.0
1996	669	(4)—	118.5
1997	(5)—	554	121.6
1998	(6)—	558	134.4
1999	712	570	124.9

The GDP deflator is a price index for all goods and services that comprise the GDP. In the above example, this index is based on price levels that existed in 1992, which are given the value 100.

The relationship between "money" GDP and "real" GDP is given by the following equation:

REAL GDP   = MONEY GDP X $\dfrac{100}{\text{GDP DEFLATOR}}$

(a)   Fill in the blanks (1 to 6) in the above table.

(b)   Money GDP includes changes due to changes in price levels and output levels. While money GDP rose by approximately 41% between 1992 and 1999, real output rose by _____% and prices rose by _____%, for the same period.

(c)   Between 1991 and 1992, money GDP _____ by _____ %, while real GDP _____ by _____%, and prices _____ by _____%.

20.   Inflation is defined as _____

_____

_____.

21.   Inflation is measured by _____

_____

_____.

22.   The Consumer Price Index is defined as _____

_____

_____.

23.   If the CPI rises from 138.2 to 143.8 over a period of one year, the rate of inflation for that year is _____ %.

24.   If the CPI at the beginning of the year is 127.2 and the rate of inflation during that year is 4%, the CPI at the end of that year would be _____.

25.   The unemployment rate expresses _____

_____.

26. If the number of employed people is 12 000 000 and the number of unemployed people is 1 167 000, the unemployment rate is _____.

27. Fill in the blanks in the table below.

Year (millions)	Labour Force (millions)	Employed (millions)	Unemployed (millions)	Unemployment Rate %
1998	13.757	12.340	1.417	10.3
1998	13.797	12.240	(a)—	11.3
2000	(b)—	12.383	(c)—	11.2

28. Suppose that Statistics Canada reported that the population of working age were 22 000 000, the labour force participation rate were 60% and there were 12 200 000 people employed.

   (a) How does Statistics Canada obtain labour-force statistics such as these?

   (b) What is the size of the *labour force*?

   (c) How many people are *unemployed*?

   (d) What is the *unemployment rate*?

29. State whether each of the following is an example of frictional, structural, seasonal, cyclical or voluntary unemployment.

   _____(a) A miner replaced by new machinery.

   _____(b) A former employee of a textile mill closed due to competition from imports.

   _____(c) A computer programmer taking two weeks of travel to British Columbia for the start of a new job.

   _____(d) A worker laid off from a fish processing plant during winter.

   _____(e) An Ontario auto worker laid off during a recession.

   _____(f) A person who is working part time for lack of full time work.

30. Match the following types of unemployment with the corresponding causes.

	Frictional	A	Reduction of economic activity during certain months.
	Seasonal	B	Downturn in the economy.
	Cyclical	C	People changing jobs.
	Structural	D	Gave up looking for work.
	Hidden	E	Mismatch of skills.

31.   "Hidden unemployment" may include

(a)   discouraged workers

(b)   workers who are employed for fewer days per week than what they would prefer.

(c)   people who accepted early retirement, but would prefer to work.

(d)   all of the above.

32.   To the extent that hidden unemployment exists,

(a)   the official unemployment rate understates the seriousness of the unemployment problem.

(b)   actual unemployment is less serious than that indicated by the official statistics.

(c)   the labour force is in reality larger than what the official statistics report.

(d)   neither the employment or unemployment figures need be challenged, in that hidden unemployment is included in the official data.

32.   How does the existence of "voluntary unemployment" affect the seriousness of the unemployment problem in Canada, as reported by the unemployment rate figures? _____

_____

_____

_____

33.   Unemployment rate statistics may misrepresent the economy's actual performance when we are either entering or leaving the recession phase in that

(a)   the unemployment rate may fall going into a recession since some workers give up looking for work.

(b)   the unemployment rate might rise when recovering from a recession since more people begin looking for work.

(c)   the unemployment rate bottoms out as the recession reaches its lowest level.

(d)   (a) and (b) above.

34.   Match the definitions on the right with the terms on the left.

	Microeconomics	A	The lowest rate of employment that can be achieved without creating inflation
	Macroeconomics	B	The maximum amount of goods and services that an economy can produce at a given time.
	Demand side of the economy	C	The value of the gross domestic product adjusted to eliminate the effect of price changes.
	Supply side of the economy	D	A measure of the total value of goods and services produced in a given time period.
	Aggregate demand	E	The gross domestic product measured in current dollar terms.
	Inflation	F	Study of output and price levels for goods in total.
	Capacity output	G	The purchasers of society's goods and services.
	Full employment	H	An overall increase in the prices of goods and services.
	Gross domestic product	I	The dollar difference between a county's total exports and total imports of goods and services.
	Net exports	J	The suppliers of society's resources.
	Real income	K	Consumer price index, which represents the overall price of a family's consumption.
	Money GDP	L	Study of output and prices of particular goods and services.
	Real GDP	M	The total of all persons both working and seeking work.
	CPI	N	A person who is seeking work (and may or may not be eligible for "EI.")
	Labour participation rate	O	The total spending on society's goods and services by all groups.
	Labour force	P	Income in terms of its purchasing power.
	Unemployed person	Q	The percentage of the working age population in the labour force.

Note. Terms reflecting types of unemployment are matched in question 30 above.

Macro Chapter 3

SOURCES OF ECONOMIC PROSPERITY:
THE SUPPLY SIDE

With the introductory chapters now complete, we begin our analysis of the operation of the economy. Essentially, we will conclude that economic prosperity is the result of a balanced interaction between the two sides of the economy:

(a) the supply side — the economy must have the ability ("productivity") to produce goods and services effectively, and

(b) the demand side — there must be sufficient demand for the economy's goods and services to enable the economy to actually operate at its potential level of output and productivity.

Chapter 3 deals with the **supply side** of the economy. The key concept on the supply side is **productivity**. Chapter 3 discusses several important factors which affect productivity, emphasizing the consumption/saving/investment relationship. How a society chooses to allocate its economic resources between **consumption** (for present enjoyment) and **saving and investment** (for future prosperity) is the most fundamental factor influencing its economic performance. These are some of the most basic and most important concepts in the field of economics, and they are relevant to today's situation. Many observers believe that excessive emphasis on current consumption (and therefore neglect of capital investment) during much of the 1960s and 1970s underlies recent problems such as the productivity slowdown and "stagflation." Only recently have governments begun to place more emphasis on managing the supply side of the economy, or what economists commonly refer to as aggregate supply (AS). Chapter 3 ends with a discussion of AS graphically illustrated as a supply curve. The reasons for its shape and the underlying causes for shifts in its position are also presented.

General Learning Objective

Examine those factors that can influence an economy's ability (potential) to produce goods and services.

Specific Learning Objectives

Self-Test

1. The most commonly-used definition of "productivity" is

    (a) the total output (GDP) of a nation

    (b) the total number of worker-hours worked per year.

    (c) profit per unit of output.

    (d) output per worker per hour.

    (e) none of the above.

2. The most important source of increased productivity is generally considered to be

    _____

    _____

    _____

3.   The basic difference between capital and consumer goods is that

(a)   capital goods cost more money than consumer goods.

(b)   the production of capital goods is the end goal of all economic activity.

(c)   capital goods are used to produce more goods, while consumer goods are intended to be used up by consumers.

(d)   capital goods are used up (depreciate) over a period of time.

(e)   capital goods are purchased by governments.

4.   The meaning of "investment" as a basic economic concept is

(a)   using society's productive resources to produce consumer goods.

(b)   putting money in the bank.

(c)   using money to make money.

(d)   using society's productive resources to produce capital goods.

5.   To an economist, the basic meaning of the concept of "saving" is

(a)   forgoing present consumption so as to free resources for possible investment.

(b)   hoarding money.

(c)   putting money in the bank.

(d)   storing consumer goods (e.g., food) for use in the future.

(e)   hoarding goods.

6.   Is it true that a society must save if it is to be able to have investment?

(a)   No, because capital goods production and consumer goods production are not in any way connected.

(b)   No, because you can borrow money to invest it — it need not be saved,

(c)   Yes, because the productive resources used to produce capital goods could have been used to produce consumer goods.

(d)   Yes, because investment involves the accumulation of consumer goods for future use.

7.   If a nation places great emphasis on capital investment, in the short run the levels of consumption enjoyed by its people will be (lower/higher) than they could have been, and in the long run they could be (lower/higher) than they would have been.

8.   The primary cost of capital investment to an economy is

     (a)   a decrease in leisure time.

     (b)   the forgone production of future goods.

     (c)   an increase in the standard of living of its citizens.

     (d)   the forgone present enjoyment of consumer goods and services.

     (e)   none of the above.

9.   Explain the reasoning behind this statement:

"For an advanced, wealthy nation, economic growth is easy; but for underdeveloped nations with a very low standard of living, economic progress is extremely difficult, if not impossible."

_____

_____

_____

_____

10.   Industrialization requires vast amounts of investment, and a correspondingly large amount of saving. Explain how such high levels of saving were achieved in

     (a)   Great Britain during the Industrial Revolution _____

_____

_____

     (b)   the Soviet Union after 1917 _____

_____

_____

11.   In addition to capital investment five possible sources of productivity are:

     (a)   _____

     (b)   _____

     (c)   _____

     (d)   _____

     (e)   _____

12.   Fill in the average and marginal tax rates.

Income	Income Tax	Average Tax Rate	Marginal Tax Rate
$30 000	$5 000	_____%	
31 000	5 300	_____%	_____%
32 000	5 650	_____%	_____%
33 000	6 050	_____%	_____%

13.   Suppose that, as a result of teaching night school, a college instructor's income increases by $1600. If he pays an additional $400 of income tax due to this extra income, his "marginal tax rate" is _____%.

14.   Carol Markotic earns $24 000 per year, on which she pays income taxes of $5000. If she works in the evenings and increases her income to $32 000, her income taxes will increase to $7000. The "marginal tax rate" paid by Carol will be _____%. The "average tax rate" paid by Carol is 20.8% on an income of $24 000. The average tax rate on the $32 000 income will be _____%.

          How would a significant increase in either of these tax rates probably affect Carol's incentive to work and save?

_____

_____

15.   "Economies of scale" are defined as _____

_____.

16.   The small size of the Canadian market relative to other nations is generally considered to

        (a)   be no obstacle to increasing productivity, because it is large enough to allow economies of scale.

        (b)   restrict the growth of productivity due to the small size of many Canadian manufacturing plants.

        (c)   restrict the growth of productivity due to the short production runs arising from the fact that one plant must often produce several different products.

        (d)   (b) and (c) together.

        (e)   be the major source of the "productivity slowdown" of recent years.

17. During the 1970s and early 1980s, real output per worker employed in Canada

    (a)   increased more rapidly than in previous years.

    (b)   generally failed to increase as in previous years, falling in some years and stagnating over the period in question.

    (c)   increased considerably, but less rapidly than in previous years.

    (d)   declined steadily.

    (e)   none of the above.

18. Low productivity generally leads to:

    (a)   higher costs and prices.

    (b)   lost sales and jobs.

    (c)   higher real income earned by workers.

    (d)   (a) and (b) above.

19. The declining rate of productivity gains in Canada during the 1980s:

    (a)   threatens jobs in Canada's export industries.

    (b)   reduces Canada's ability to compete effectively with the US under the Free Trade Agreement.

    (c)   results in an increase in the demand for labour in Canada's industry.

    (d)   (a) and (b) above.

20. What is the effect of a slowdown in worker productivity?

    (a)   a decline in the purchasing power of wage earners' incomes.

    (b)   a decline in living standards.

    (c)   a failure of wage increases to keep up with the inflation rate.

    (d)   all of the above.

21. According to the Centre for the Study of Living Standards, the productivity gap between Canada and the U.S. had been (widening, narrowing) since the 1990's. Indeed, Canada's productivity in manufacturing had improved in total but, in comparative terms to the U.S, had slipped from _____ percent in 1994 to about _____ percent of the U.S. level in 2001.

22. During the 1990's the Canadian manufacturing grew mainly by _____, whereas the U.S. economy grew mainly by _____.

23. Two other reasons for the productivity differences in manufacturing between Canada and the U.S. have been attributed to _____ and _____ ..

24. Explain how the difference in "high tech" involvement contributed to the U.S. / Canada productivity gap in manufacturing.

     _____

     _____

     _____

     _____

25. List five ways that governments in Canada have attempted to influence productivity:

     1. _____

     2. _____

     3. _____

     4. _____

     5. _____

26. How would productivity in the Canadian economy probably be affected by a free trade agreement with several other nations? Give two reasons for your answer.

     _____

     _____

     _____

     _____

27. "Aggregate supply" is defined as _____

     _____

     _____

28.

Cost per Unit of Output	Volume of Output
$2	10
2	20
2	50
3	60
4	70
5	80
6	90
7	100
8	100
10	100

Using the above data plot an aggregate supply curve on the graph below.

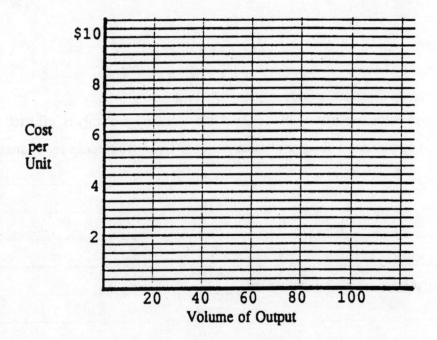

29.   State whether each of the following statements concerning aggregate supply is **TRUE** or **FALSE**.

_____ (a)   The most basic cause of a decrease in aggregate supply is a rise in the cost of producing goods and services.

_____ (b)   Supply side economists generally advocate policies that encourage households to work, save and invest.

_____ (c)   A decrease in aggregate supply will generally benefit the country.

_____ (d)   An increase in aggregate supply will increase the volume of output and decrease cost levels.

_____ (e)   The aggregate supply curve shows the total quantity of goods and services that will be produced (supplied) at different cost levels.

30.   The rising portion of an AS curve indicates that

(a)   production costs are rising.

(b)   increases in output are accompanied by increases in costs per unit.

(c)   some industries may be experiencing production "bottlenecks."

(d)   all of the above.

(e)   none of the above.

31.   The AS curve will likely shift to the right if

(a)   factor input costs decline.

(b)   efficiency has improved.

(c)   an economy's resource base has increased.

(d)   all of the above.

(e)   (b) and (c) above.

32.   The AS curve will shift upward to the left if

(a)   the government makes available a tax incentive.

(b)   new entrants to the labour force are better trained.

(c)   worker productivity decreases.

(d)   production costs per unit decrease.

(e)   none of the above.

33.   If the average wage rate throughout the economy were to decline,

(a)   production costs would increase per unit of output.

(b)   producers would raise prices.

(c)   production would decline.

(d)   none of the above.

(e)   (a) and (c) above.

34. Match the definitions on the left with the terms on the right.

	Supply side of the economy	A	The use of the economy's resources to produce goods and services.
	Demand side of the economy	B	Taxes levied on the amount of a corporation's assets.
	Productivity	C	Goods used by consumers for present use.
	Consumption Goods	D	The production of capital goods that makes possible increased production in the future.
	Capital goods	E	A measure of efficiency, usually output per worker.
	Investment	F	The purchasers of society's goods and services.
	Savings	G	The percentage of any additional income received that goes to tax.
	Economies of Scale	H	Doing without consumer goods.
	Marginal tax Rate	I	The ability to reduce the cost per unit with operations of larger size, due to more capital and technology.
	Capital tax	J	The relationship between production cost per unit and the level of output.
	Aggregate supply curve	K	Building and equipment; goods used to produce other goods.

Macro Chapter 4

SOURCES OF ECONOMIC PROSPERITY:
THE DEMAND SIDE

In this chapter, our focus shifts from the supply side of the economy to the demand side. The key concept on the demand side is "aggregate demand," or total spending on goods and services. Prosperity requires a balanced interaction between the supply side and the demand side of the economy, with aggregate demand neither too low nor too high relative to the economy's ability to produce goods and services.

If aggregate demand is too low, the result will be classic "recession," with output, employment and prices all depressed. If aggregate demand is excessively high, the economy will suffer from classic "inflation," as high demand generates not only high levels of output and employment, but also rapidly rising prices. Thus, ideally, aggregate demand would be high enough to generate high levels of output and employment, but not so high as to generate too rapid inflation: this would represent the balanced interaction between the supply side and the demand side of the economy referred to in the preceding paragraph.

Chapter 4 inevitably creates some confusion among students with regard to the role of saving in the economy. Chapter 3 presents saving as a good thing, essential to investment and prosperity. Now, Chapter 4 seems to suggest that saving is a bad thing, because it reduces aggregate demand, and thus could cause a recession. Which is correct? Would the economy benefit from more saving or less? There is no simple answer to this question, as it depends on the balance between saving and investment. An increase in saving that was not offset by higher investment would not only depress aggregate demand, but also would contribute to lower future productivity and prosperity. Thus, the economy needs a balance between consumption and saving and investment: there should be enough consumption to purchase the output which the economy can currently produce (and thus avoid a recession today), as well as enough saving to finance capital investment (and thus increase future prosperity).

General Learning Objective

To explore the role of total spending (i.e., the "demand side") as a determinant of economic prosperity.

Specific Learning Objectives

Self-Test

Reference

1. Recognize the components of aggregate demand. .... #1-4
2. Demonstrate the equality of GDP and total incomes. .... #5
3. Examine the role of savings in an economy. .... #6, 9
4. Describe the key condition that results in GDP being at equilibrium................. #10
5. Assess the effect on GDP when planned savings is either less than or
    greater than planned investment. .... #11-14
6. Demonstrate the effect on GDP of other leakages and injections. .... #15, 16
7. Demonstrate how the interaction of aggregate demand and aggregate
    supply affect the performance of the economy... #17-22
8. Review the terms used in the chapter. .... #23

Self-Test

1. "Aggregate demand" is defined as _____
    _____, and consists of four components:
    _____, _____,
    _____, and _____.

2. The largest component of aggregate demand in Canada is _____
    and the smallest is _____.

3. (a) Consumption spending buys about _____% of GDP.

(b)   The main factor that determines the amount of consumption spending is

_____

(c)   Other factors that affect the amount of consumption spending include

_____ and _____

4. (a)   Investment spending by business amounts to about _____% of GDP.

(b)   State whether each of the following would cause business investment

spending to *rise* or *fall*:

(i)   an increase in interest rates: _____

(ii)   economic forecasts that the economy will grow quite rapidly over

the next 2–3 years: _____

(iii)   an increase in taxes on business profits: _____

5. Consider the following statements:

(a)   "Aggregate demand can never be sufficient to purchase all the goods and

services an economy is capable of producing, since total income payments

will fall short of the value of production."

(b)   "Aggregate demand is always sufficient to purchase all goods and services

an economy is capable of producing, since total income payments will be

equal to the value of production."

Are either of the above quotations correct? Explain:

_____

_____

_____

_____

6. "Saving" is a possible source of economic difficulties because

(a)   too much saving causes inflation.

(b)   savings lead to speculation in the stock market.

(c)   the rich people who save a great deal get richer due to their investment

income.

(d)   it can cause an economic slowdown due to inadequate demand for goods

and services.

(e)   none of the above.

7.   The problem referred to in the previous question will not occur if

   (a)   money that is saved is invested in the stock market.

   (b)   money that is saved is deposited in banks.

   (c)   money that is saved is transferred to businesses and used to purchase capital goods.

   (d)   the government places a tax on savings.

   (e)   none of the above.

8.   Saving can actually help the economy to grow, if _____

_____

_____

9.   If all the spenders in an economy simultaneously try to save more, the resulting change in national income will pull savings (up/down). This prediction is commonly referred to as the _____.

10.   If planned investment is equal to planned savings, GDP and total income will tend to _____.

11.   If planned investment is less than planned savings, GDP and total income will tend to _____.

12.   The effect described in the previous question will occur because

   (a)   output is depressed.

   (b)   prices are depressed and output remains stable.

   (c)   output rises.

   (d)   prices and output rise.

   (e)   prices and/or output are depressed.

13.   If planned investment is greater than planned savings, GDP and total incomes will tend to _____.

14.   The effect described in the previous question will occur because

   (a)   prices and output are depressed.

   (b)   prices and/or output rise.

   (c)   prices rise and output remains stable.

   (d)   output is depressed.

   (e)   output rises.

15.   If all other things remain constant:

    (a)   an increase in taxes will cause GDP to _____.

    (b)   a decrease in taxes will cause GDP to _____.

    (c)   a decrease in government spending will cause GDP to _____.

    (d)   an increase in investment spending will cause GDP to _____.

16.   Fill in the blanks:

    (a)   If leakages exceed injections, then AD, output, employment and prices

        will _____ and the economy will likely _____.

    (b)   If $(I + G + X) > (S + T + M)$ then AD will _____ and

        the economy will _____.

    (c)   If leakages _____ injections then the economy will likely

        remain stable.

17.

AD		AD1	
Price Level	**Volume Output**	**Price Level**	**Volume Output**
$8	50%	$10	70%
6	60	8	80
4	70	6	90
2	80	4	100
2	90		

Using the above data, plot two aggregate demand curves (AD and AD1) on the graph below. Volume is expressed as a percent of capacity.

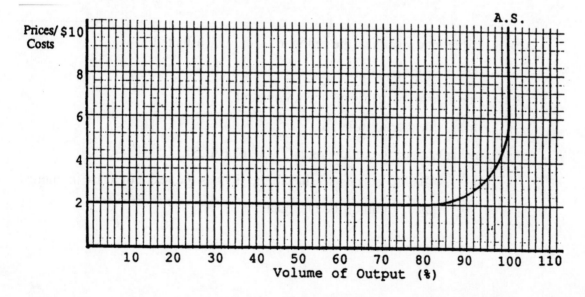

The resulting shift in the above AD curve (AD to AD1) is likely to

(a)   (increase/decrease) price levels.

(b)   (increase/decrease) real GDP.

(c)   (increase/decrease) unemployment.

(d)   (increase/decrease) incomes.

(e)   (increase/decrease) interest rates.

(f)   (increase/decrease) consumption.

18.   Explain or illustrate on the graph in Question 17 how inflation (rising prices) caused by an increase in AD might have been reduced or avoided.

_____

_____

_____

_____

19.   Suppose that the economy were operating well below its potential ("capacity") output. Suppose also that interest rates fell and there were expectations that economic conditions were going to improve.

(a)   Explain how and why these developments would likely affect aggregate demand in the economy. _____

_____

_____

_____

_____

(b)   Explain how each of the following would be affected:

(i)   output

(ii)   employment and unemployment

(iii)   the rate of inflation.

20.   State whether each of the following is TRUE or FALSE.

_____(a)   The AD curve will shift to the right as the result of a rise in interest rates, all things being equal.

_____(b) Demand management and supply side policies aimed at influencing AD and AS can be used to reduce the effects of unemployment and inflation.

_____(c) The AD curve shows the total quantity of goods and services that will be demanded at different price levels.

_____(d) A right shift in the AD curve in the vertical portion of the AS curve will result in an increase in the volume of output.

_____(e) A decrease in aggregate supply generally results in unemployment and inflation.

_____(f) If consumers spend less, then AD falls, the AD curve shifts to the left, the volume of output falls and price levels remain stable on the horizontal portion of the AS curve.

21.   During a recession,

(a) aggregate demand is depressed, causing output, employment and prices to fall.

(b) aggregate demand is depressed and output and employment rise, causing prices to fall

(c) aggregate demand is depressed, causing output and employment to be depressed and prices to rise.

(d) prices fall, causing aggregate demand to rise and output and employment to rise.

(e) prices rise, causing output, employment and aggregate demand to fall.

22.   During an economic boom,

(a) prices rise, causing aggregate demand, output and employment to fall.

(b) prices fall, causing output, employment and aggregate demand to rise.

(c) aggregate demand rises, causing output and employment to rise, which causes prices to fall.

(d) aggregate demand rises and output and employment fall, causing prices to rise.

(e) aggregate demand rises, causing output, employment and prices to rise.

23.   Match the definitions on the right with the terms on the left.

	Demand side of the economy	A	An overall (or average) increase in the prices of goods and services.
	Aggregate demand	B	Personal disposable income that is not consumed.
	Consumption spending	C	Consumer debt as a percentage of disposable income.
	Personal disposable income	D	Same as business savings (profits that are held by the business).
	Consumer confidence	E	The percentage of personal disposable income that is saved.
	Interest rate	F	Personal income after taxes are deducted.
	Consumer indebtedness	G	The maximum potential output on the supply side of the economy.
	Personal saving	H	The purchasers of society's output of goods and services.
	Personal saving rate	I	The degree to which consumers are optimistic about their future economic prospects.
	Business savings	J	The price of money expressed as a percentage of money borrowed.
	Retained earnings	K	Spending by households on consumer goods and services.
	Capacity output	L	Total spending on goods and services.
	Inflation	M	Same as retained earnings (business profit after taxes and dividends have been paid).

Macro Chapter 5

MONEY AND THE ECONOMIC SYSTEM

This chapter deals with money: what it is and how it is created. In Canada, coins, bank notes and bank deposits are used as money, with the vast majority of money taking the form of bank deposits, which are transferred between people and businesses by cheques. These deposits are created through the lending activities of the banking system, which is able to create large volumes of bank deposits on the basis of relatively small cash reserves.

In our study of Macroeconomics, we have stressed the importance of the level of aggregate demand to the performance of the economy. Obviously, the volume of money in circulation (the "money supply") strongly influences the level of aggregate demand, making it essential that neither too little nor too much money be created, which could cause recession or inflation, respectively. Unfortunately, it is not easy to define and measure the money supply as precisely as we would like, because there are different definitions of "money" and thus different measures of the money supply. M1 includes only immediately spendable funds, while M2 and M2+ include various types of savings deposits. These funds could be converted into immediately spendable deposits on quite short notice, thus adding greatly to the level of aggregate demand. There is general agreement on the importance of the money supply to the level of aggregate demand and the performance of the economy. There is continuing discussion on how to actually measure the money supply.

General Learning Objective

Describe the origin and role of money in today's economy.

Specific Learning Objectives

Self-Test

1.   The volume of money in circulation ("money supply") is important to the performance of the economy because _____ _____ _____.

2.   If the money supply is too small, the result will be _____ while an excessively large money supply will cause _____.

3.   The three functions of money are:

(a)   _____

(b)   _____

(c)   _____

4. Each of the following transactions demonstrates a particular function of money. Match a function from the previous question with a transaction.

   (a) a hairstylist adds up her gratuities for the day

   (b) M. and Mme. Laframboise purchase an Inuit carving

   (c) Bobby puts one-half of his weekly allowance in his piggy bank

   (d) a homemaker buys $150 worth of groceries a week

   (e) Reza works for a fast food outlet for minimum wage after school and on weekends

5. The basic requirement of "money" is that it be

   (a) authorized by the central government as legal tender.

   (b) backed by precious metals.

   (c) generally accepted as a medium of exchange.

   (d) some sort of credit or debt.

6. Define the following additional characteristics of money.

   (a) the ability to make change _____

   (b) coins don't wear out easily _____

   (c) limited supply _____

   (d) easy to carry _____

7. State whether each of the following statements concerning precious metals is **TRUE** or **FALSE**.

   _____ (a) Gold is a precious metal.

   _____ (b) Debased coinage will cause inflation.

   _____ (c) Coins are exchanged for their intrinsic value rather than their face value.

   _____ (d) Debasing coinage increases its purchasing power.

   _____ (e) A 1956 Canadian silver dollar has an intrinsic value that exceeds its face value.

8. State whether each of the following statements concerning bank notes in Canada is **TRUE** or **FALSE**.

   _____ (a) They are issued by the Bank of Canada, which is a federal government agency

_____ (b) They are backed by gold.

_____ (c) They represent a promise by the government to pay money to the holder of the note.

_____ (d) They declare the notes to be legal tender.

_____ (e) They comprise more than half of Canada's money supply.

9. State whether each of the following statements concerning demand deposits in Canada is TRUE or FALSE.

_____ (a) They represent the deposits of cash (notes and coins) made into depositors' accounts and held on their behalf by the bank.

_____ (b) They are transferred between depositors' accounts according to instructions written on cheques.

_____ (c) They represent the largest single form of money.

_____ (d) They are not really money.

_____ (e) They are money, but represent a small proportion of the money supply.

10. Cheques are

(a) the means by which approximately 90% of the volume of money is transacted.

(b) instructions to banks to transfer money (bank deposits) from one person to another.

(c) valueless if there are insufficient funds in the account.

(d) not money.

(e) all of the above.

11. State whether each of the following is regarded as money, near money or neither.

(a) a department store credit card _____

(b) a corporate bond _____

(c) a $20 Bank of Canada bank note _____

(d) a gold coin _____

(e) a $500 Canada Savings Bond _____

(f) a chequable bank deposit _____

(g) a Government of Canada child tax benefit cheque _____

(h) $10 worth of pennies _____

(i)   a work of art _____

(j)   a savings account _____

(k)   a share of Bank of Montreal stock _____

12.   As a percentage of M2, Canada's money supply consists of approximately

_____ % cash (bank notes and coins in circulation) and _____ %

book entries (deposits).

13.   State whether each of the following statements concerning M1 is TRUE or

FALSE.

_____(a)   It is the narrowest definition of the money supply.

_____(b)   It includes currency (notes and coins) outside the banking system.

_____(c)   It includes demand deposits (current chequing accounts).

_____(d)   It includes chequable personal savings deposits.

_____(e)   It was the official measure of the money supply used by the federal

government from 1975 to 1982.

14.   **M1** includes _____

_____.

15.   **M2** includes M1 plus

(a)   deposits backed by gold.

(b)   fiat money held by foreigners.

(c)   non-personal notice deposits.

(d)   term deposits.

(e)   none of the above.

16.   M2+ includes M2 Plus _____

_____

17.   From the data below, in billions of dollars calculate:

(a) M1 _____ (b) M2 _____   (c) M2+ _____

Foreign currency deposits	$2
Demand deposits	15
Deposits at trust and mortgage loan companies	30
Personal savings deposits	50

Non-personal notice deposits	30
Cash in bank safe	3
Currency outside banks	10
Deposits in credit unions and caisses populaires	15
Money market mutual funds	12

18. Canada's money supply is backed

   (a)   dollar for dollar by gold.

   (b)   by 8 cents of gold per dollar.

   (c)   by silver as well as gold.

   (d)   by the nation's ability to compete in international markets.

   (e)   by people's faith in its purchasing power.

19. The measure of the money supply that moves most closely with the level of aggregate demand for Canadian goods and services is either _____ or _____.

20. The vast majority of Canada's money supply consists of _____ which are created by _____ _____.

21. Banks are able to operate safely with their deposits far in excess of their cash reserves because

   (a)   they are owned by the federal government.

   (b)   their cash withdrawals tend to be offset by cash deposits.

   (c)   most financial transactions are by cheque, and require no withdrawals of cash from the banks.

   (d)   (b) and (c) above.

   (e)   (a) and (b) above.

22. If a bank has $10 million in total reserves and holds $8.1 million as desired reserves, then it can lend out _____.

23. If the financial institutions increase their cash reserves from 5% to 10%, then the money supply will _____.

24.   There are two factors that influence the decision of financial institutions regarding
        how much cash reserves to maintain against deposits — the safety factor and the
        desire to earn interest on deposits.

        The safety factor acts to _____ (decrease, increase) cash reserves
        whereas the desire to earn a return on loans and other investments tends to
        _____ (increase, decrease) cash reserves.

        In reality, a small amount of cash reserves are supporting a large amount
        of deposits. The main reason why this is possible is _____.

25.   Suppose that financial institutions maintain a 5% cash reserve against deposits.
        Now, Bank I receives new cash deposits of $100,000. Bank I increases their loans
        by _____ and maintains cash reserves of _____. The borrowers
        spend the money and the proceeds of the loans end up in Trust Company A.
        Deposits in Trust Company A increase by _____ so they increase their
        loans by _____ and maintain _____ of cash reserves
        against these deposits. If the process continues and each institution lends out 95%
        of new deposits, the total increase in deposits for all financial institutions as a
        result of the initial $100 000 deposit is approaching _____.

26.   What happens to Canada's money supply when

        (a)   cash is deposited into a bank?

        (b)   a loan is paid off?

        (c)   a transfer is made between bank accounts?

        (d)   cash is withdrawn from a savings account?

        (e)   a bank lends money?

        (f)   a Canada Savings Bond is redeemed for cash?

27.   Canada's chartered banks are

        (a)   privately owned corporations (owned by stockholders).

        (b)   owned and operated by the federal government.

        (c)   regulated by the federal government, particularly with respect to their
                lending activities.

        (d)   (a) and (c) above.

(e) owned and operated by the provincial governments in accordance with federal regulations.

28. Government regulation of the banking system is intended to

(a) limit the profits of the banks.

(b) promote increased lending and more rapid increases in the money supply during periods of recession.

(c) avoid excessive increases in lending and the money supply which could generate inflation.

(d) (b) and (c) above.

(e) all of the above.

29. Explain how a privately owned banking system can contribute to the problem of economic instability.

_____

_____

_____

_____

_____

_____

30. If the banking system creates too much money, the likely result is future _____. On the other hand, if the banking system creates too little money, the economy could fall into _____.

31. Match the terms on the left with the definitions on the right.

	Money Supply	A	The amount of cash kept on hand by a bank to cover day to day withdrawals of cash
	M1	B	The percentage of total deposits that a bank keeps as cash reserves.
	M2	C	The narrowest definitions of the money supply, including only currency plus demand deposits.
	M2+	D	A wider definition of the money supply, including M1 plus personal savings deposits plus non personal notice deposits.
	Cash Reserves	E	The total volume of money in circulation, defined variously M1, M2, and M2+
	Cash Reserve Ratio.	F	A wider definition of money supply including M2 plus deposits at trust and mortgage loan companies, credit unions and caisses populaires.

Macro Chapter 6

Booms, Recessions, and Inflation

Chapter 6 examines a long-standing problem associated with market economies: fluctuations in economic activity (business cycles), in which the economy alternates between periods of rapid expansion and recessions. These business cycles arise from fluctuations in aggregate demand, which in turn generate fluctuations in output, employment and price levels.

These fluctuations in aggregate demand arise from various factors, which are identified as fluctuations in investment spending, the "multiplier effect," the "accelerator effect" and fluctuations in export demand. While these factors can be separated for purposes of analysis, the separation is in reality quite artificial. Actually, it is the dynamic interaction of all of these factors which generates business cycles. For instance, in any recession, depressed investment spending and depressed consumption spending are each partly the cause and partly the result of the recession: through the "multiplier" and "accelerator" effects, each is related to the other, partly as a cause and partly as a result.

Chapter 6 places particular emphasis on the recession side of business cycles, leaving the problem of inflation to be examined later. Also, in order to present the problem of business cycles as simply and clearly as possible, Chapter 6 omits any reference to the government sector of the economy and the government's likely responses to economic downturns. The role of the government in dealing with business cycles will be covered in Chapter 7, as our coverage of the operation of the economy becomes more complete.

General Learning Objective

Consider the reasons for fluctuations in economic activity.

Specific Learning Objectives

		Self-Test Reference
1.	Recognize the four phases of the business cycle	#1, 2
2.	Review the development of business cycle theories and recognize the importance of aggregate demand as a source of cyclical fluctuations	#3
3.	Account for the instability of investment spending	#4-6
4.	Develop the theory of the multiplier, demonstrate its contribution to economic instability, and identify the size of the Canadian multiplier	#7-13
5.	Consider the "accelerator effect" as a cause of cyclical swings, and demonstrate the effect of a combined accelerator-multiplier reaction	#14-23
6.	Profile an economic boom and an economic recession	#24-28
7.	Examine the approaches to economic forecasting	#29
8.	Recognize the key terms used in this Chapter	#30

Self-Test

1. Identify the phase of the business cycle indicated by each of the following:

    _____ (a) Unemployment is rising, consumer spending is at comparatively low levels.

    _____ (b) Both employment and real investment are rising.

    _____ (c) Inflation is at its highest level and output is considered to be at maximum.

    _____ (d) Unemployment has peaked, economic activity is at its slowest, and prices are depressed but stable.

2. The sequence "expansion — peak — contraction — trough":

    (a) indicates four distinct business cycles.

    (b) indicates four distinct phases of a single business cycle.

    (c) indicates two distinct business cycles — an upswing and a downswing.

    (d) indicates four phases of four business cycles.

3.   The most likely cause of business cycles is _____

      _____.

4.   Investment spending tends to be the most variable of the components of aggregate demand since:

      (a)   residential construction activity changes substantially between periods of economic expansion and recession.

      (b)   investment spending decisions are based on business expectations of future sales and profits.

      (c)   businesses attempt to reduce their inventory investment when recessions are expected.

      (d)   inventory levels increase during boom periods.

      (e)   all of the above.

5.   Which of the following components of business investment is considered to be the most variable?

      (a)   production of equipment.

      (b)   construction.

      (c)   additions to business inventories.

      (d)   no single component is more variable than any other.

6.   Which of the following best describes the effect of changes in business investment on the economy?

      (a)   The leakage of saving is fairly steady, and fluctuations in investment can mean that leakages are not matched by injections, causing economic activity to fluctuate.

      (b)   Although business investment is an injection, leakages of the same magnitude can be expected to offset the injections, resulting in economic stability.

      (c)   An increase in investment will automatically cause savings to increase, thereby resulting in a decline in economic activity.

7.   The size of the multiplier depends on _____

      _____

      _____

8.   The greater the "leakages" from respending, the smaller the multiplier effect. The three leakages from respending are _____ ,

_____ ,

and _____ .

9.   If 40% of increases in income are respent, the size of the multiplier will be

_____ .

10.   The multiplier effect tends to

      (a)   smooth out upswings and downswings in business activity.

      (b)   cause a small change in investment to result in a considerably larger change in GDP and total incomes.

      (c)   slow down the growth of the economy.

      (d)   make price levels more stable.

      (e)   operate more strongly in economic upswings than in downswings.

11.   A multiplier of 3 implies that when

      (a)   investment increases by $3, GDP and total incomes increase by $1.

      (b)   investment increases by $1, GDP and total incomes increase by $3.

      (c)   investment increases by $1, consumption increases by $3.

      (d)   consumption increases by $3, investment increases by $1.

      (e)   consumption increases by $1, investment increases by $3.

12.   Because of the pure water and the transportation access, a company builds a distillery in rural Manitoba. In the first year of operation, the company employs two hundred local people and pays out a total wage and salary bill of $6 million. After personal saving, taxes and the purchase of imports, the distillery workers spend $2 million on domestic consumer goods and services.

      (a)   The multiplier is _____ .

      (b)   Suppose the owners of the business invest $9 million in new machinery and equipment for the distillery. Over time, what is the total effect on the area's income? Also, show the first 3 stages of the multiplier effect.

             Initial investment spending $_____

             Stage 1 of respending $_____

             Stage 2 of respending $_____

TOTAL CHANGE IN INCOME (End of Stage 2): $_____

TOTAL CHANGE IN INCOME (End of Series): $_____

(c)   If the multiplier had been 2.5, then the total change in income in part (b) would be $_____.

13.   The best estimate of the Canadian multiplier for a one-year period is

_____.

14.   The "accelerator effect" refers to a situation in which

(a)   a fall in the demand for capital goods will cause the demand for consumer goods to fall.

(b)   without increased government spending, the economy will collapse.

(c)   increases in incomes are partially respent, causing larger increases in GDP and total incomes.

(d)   an increase in the demand for consumer goods causes an increase in the demand for capital goods.

(e)   none of the above.

15.   The condition that must exist if the accelerator effect is to operate is that

_____

16.   "Induced investment" refers to _____

_____

_____.

17.   For the level of induced investment to be maintained, consumer spending must

_____

18.   If consumer spending rises more slowly than in the past, induced investment will

_____.

19.   Suppose a company maintains $3 of capital for every $1 of sales. If current sales are $1 million, the desired level of capital is _____. If sales rise to $3 million, desired capital is _____. Ignoring the effects of capital consumption, this means that new investment for this company is

_____.

20.   The effect of the accelerator on the economy is to

(a)   make the demand for capital goods more stable.

(b)   reduce consumer spending.

(c)   ensure that the economy will continue to grow steadily.

(d)   smooth out the economic fluctuations associated with the business cycle.

(e)   make the demand for capital goods even more unstable.

21.   Economists estimate that when the multiplier effect and the accelerator effect are combined, an increase in investment spending of $80 million can cause GDP and total incomes to rise between $_____ million and $_____.

22.   Suppose that the distillery described in Question 13 has the following levels of sales. The owners wish to maintain a constant capital to sales ratio.

Year	Sales	Capital	Investment
1998	$12 million	$30 million	
1999	$15 million	_____	_____
2000	$20 million	_____	_____

Answer parts (a) and (b) to fill in the table.

(a)   Assuming no lags in investment spending, determine the desired level of capital for the Years 1999 and 2000.

(b)   As a result of the new capital requirements, what is the level of investment spending (excluding depreciation of existing capital) for the years 1999 and 2000?

(c)   In 2001, distillery sales remain at $20 million. Determine the following:

Required capital for this level of sales _____.

New investment required _____.

(d)   Based on Questions (a) through (c), determine the expansion years and the recession years.

1999   _____

2000   _____

2001   _____

23.   The previous question demonstrated the accelerated effects of investment spending in response to increased yearly sales. We must remember that the

multiplier is still to be considered in this analysis as strengthening the
expansionary phases of the business cycle of 1998 and 2000 and adding to the
recessionary tendencies of 2001.

Assuming a multiplier of 2, complete the following table using the
investment spending from Question 22 to confirm the interaction of accelerator
and multiplier.

Year	Investment Spending	Change in Income
1999	_____	_____
2000	_____	_____
2001	_____	_____

24. During recessions, which is most likely to decline sharply?

(a) household spending on consumer goods.

(b) government spending on goods and services.

(c) consumer spending on services.

(d) business spending on capital goods.

(e) municipal government spending.

25. Which of the following are likely to happen during a typical economic boom?

_____ (a) Housing sales increase rapidly.

_____ (b) Capital investment spending by business increases more rapidly
          than usual

_____ (c) The prices of goods and services in general increase more rapidly
          than usual.

_____ (d) Automobile sales increase rapidly.

_____ (e) Interest rates decline.

26. Which of the following are likely to happen during a typical economic recession?

_____ (a) Automobile sales decrease.

_____ (b) Interest rates decline.

_____ (c) Housing sales are depressed.

_____ (d) The prices of goods and services in general increase more rapidly
          than usual.

_____ (e) Unemployment increases.

27. During a recession, which one of the following would most likely experience unemployment?

    (a)   teachers   (d)   lawyers

    (b)   brewers   (e)   bricklayers

    (c)   managers

28. Suppose that the economy has been growing rapidly for several years and that the unemployment rate is now the lowest it has been in a decade and is still falling.

    (a)   What kinds of economic forces would be *causing* such a situation?

    (b)   What sort of *problems* would you expect in an economy in this situation?

    (c)   Would you expect that the next change in interest rates would be an *increase* or a *decrease*? Why?

    (d)   What would you expect to be the direction that the economy described here would take over the next two or three years, and why?

29. Briefly describe two approaches used to prepare economic forecasts:

    (1)   _____

    _____

    (2)   _____

    _____

30. Match the terms on the left with the definitions on the right.

	Business Cycle	A	The expansion phase of the business cycle, characterized by rapid increases in output and employment.
	Boom	B	The fluctuations of the economy between prosperity and recession.
	Multiplier Effect	C	The effect whereby rising consumption spending causes rapid increases in induced investment, and slowing down or leveling off of consumption spending causes sharp declines in induced investment.
	Accelerator	D	Capital investment spending undertaken by business in response to increases in sales that have brought production to near-capacity levels and that are expected to continue.
	Induced Investment	E	People's expectation of future inflation that leads them to seek larger wage increases and to make purchases of some big-ticket items quickly, before prices rise further.

	Inflation Psychology	F	An economic statistic that tends to increase or decrease in advance of increases or decreases in the pace of economic activity, thus giving advance notice of changes in economic trends.
	Recession Psychology	G	The effect whereby fluctuations in spending (for instance, investment spending) spread by means of the responding effect through the economy, with the total impact on GDP and incomes being considerably larger than the initial fluctuations in spending.
	Leading Economic Indicator	H	People's concerns regarding recession and unemployment that lead them to curtail their spending especially on big-ticket items that require borrowing.

Macro Chapter 7

STABILIZING THE ECONOMY: GOVERNMENT MONETARY AND FISCAL POLICIES

This chapter introduces the concept that the performance of the entire economy can be influenced by government policies, which affect the level of aggregate demand. In particular, "fiscal policy" uses budget deficits to stimulate aggregate demand in order to combat recessions; budget surpluses are used as an anti-inflationary policy to dampen aggregate demand. Chapter 7 emphasizes the use of budget deficits to stimulate the economy, leaving anti-inflation policies to a later chapter.

Chapter 7 deals with how the government, through the Bank of Canada, exercises control over the size and the rate of growth of the money supply. This "monetary policy" is directed toward the same objectives as "fiscal policy." Monetary policy affects the level of aggregate demand so as to influence the performance of the economy.

One source of difficulty in Chapter 7 tends to be the "open-market" operations of the Bank of Canada. In studying this it can be helpful to focus first on Bank of Canada purchases of securities from and sales of securities to the chartered banks. When the bonds are paid for, the transactions have a direct effect on the banks' deposits (reserves) at the Bank of Canada, and thus on their lending activities. In the more complex case of bond purchases from and sales to the public, the final result is the same: the complexity arises from the fact that there are more steps in between. The key thing to remember here is that the public does not deal directly with the Bank of Canada; rather, the chartered banks act as an intermediary in these transactions. Thus the Bank of Canada's cheques to the public are honoured by the banks, and the Bank of Canada compensates the banks by increasing their deposits (= reserves) at the Bank of Canada. Similarly, when a private individual writes cheques to the Bank of Canada the funds do not go directly from the individual's account to the Bank of Canada; rather, they go from the private account to the banks, with the banks deposits (= reserves) at the Bank of Canada being reduced by the same amount to compensate. The net result is a flow of funds from the public through the banks, to the Bank of Canada, and lower cash reserves for the banks.

To finance its budget deficits, the government normally borrows funds through bond issues, thereby incurring a "National Debt." Properly managed deficits and debt can have beneficial effects on the economy, and have become an accepted part of government economic policy. However, both economic theory and recent experience suggest that **excessively large** budget deficits can harm the economy's performance. If such deficits are financed by "printing money" on a large scale, it is obvious that severe inflation will result. A more subtle problem can occur if such deficits are financed by borrowing — the result of this can be economic **stagnation**, as the economy, productivity and living standards fail to grow. This seems to contradict everything that we have said about budget deficits, which are supposed to **stimulate** aggregate demand and the economy. However, the problem with excessive government deficits and borrowing occurs on the supply side of the economy. The economy only generates a certain volume of saving in any given year, so if government borrowing absorbs too much of these savings, fewer funds will be available for capital investment by private business, which can be "crowded out" by government borrowing. In effect, then, excessive government borrowing for spending on consumption purposes (tax cuts, social welfare programs and so on) can shift the allocation of society's economic resources away from investment and toward consumption, and thus increase current prosperity at the expense of future prosperity. While such excessive government budget deficits may stimulate the demand side of the economy, they can undermine capital investment (the supply side), stagnating growth. Since the mid-1970s and into the 1990s there have been concerns that this could be a problem in the Canadian economy, as the federal government's commitments regarding its taxation and expenditure programs have resulted in persistently large budget deficits and massive borrowing.

General Learning Objectives

Distinguish different tools of monetary policy and explain how these tools would be used under different economic conditions

Examine the use of monetary and fiscal policy to stimulate economic activity and growth.

Specific Learning Objectives

		Self-Test Reference
1.	Recognize the nature of regulation of the banking system	#1-4
2.	Explain the fundamental nature of the Bank of Canada	#5
3.	Understand the appropriate use of monetary policy under varying economic conditions	#6-9
4.	Understand the complementary nature of monetary and fiscal policy	#10-16
5.	Define "fiscal policy"	#17
6.	Apply fiscal policy to stimulate the economy	#18-27
7.	Demonstrate the reinforcement made to fiscal policy by the multiplier and accelerator effects	#28
8.	Consider the choices government may make with respect to financing a deficit budget	#29, 30
9.	Define the National Debt and establish the reasons for its accumulation	#31-33
10.	Examine the record and the causes of federal deficits and rising National Debt since 1975	#34
11.	Establish the major concerns which massive federal deficits and a mounting National Debt have given rise to since 1975	#35-39
12.	Consider the alternatives by which the federal government's budget may be reduced during the 1990s	#40-42
13.	Recognize the key terms used in this chapter	#43

Self-Test

1. The danger of a privately owned banking system that is not regulated by the government is that

    (a)   banks will generally tend to lose money due to poor lending policies.

    (b)   it will operate less efficiently than a government-operated system.

    (c)   it will generally not make enough loans to keep the economy moving.

    (d)   it will worsen the problem of economic instability by making too many loans during periods of inflation and too few loans during recessions.

    (e)   none of the above.

2. State whether it is TRUE or FALSE that the federal government regulates the Canadian banking system in each of the following ways:

    _____ (a)   The ability of the chartered banks to make a loan is controlled by the Bank of Canada.

    _____ (b)   All banks are required to provide insurance on deposits.

    _____ (c)   There are special requirements which must be met before a new chartered bank can be formed.

    _____ (d)   The chartered banks are owned and operated by the federal government, through the Bank of Canada.

    _____ (e)   There are limits on the profits which banks may earn.

    _____ (f)   There are limits on the fees which the banks may charge the public for their services (e.g., cheque charges).

3. A chartered bank is _____

    _____

4. Canada's money supply is controlled by

    (a)   the provincial governments.

    (b)   the International Monetary Fund.

    (c)   the federal government, through the Bank of Canada.

    (d)   Parliament.

    (e)   the chartered banks.

5. The Bank of Canada is owned by _____; its

    basic role is _____.

6. If the Bank of Canada sells $20 million in government bonds to the public, the

    cash reserves of the banks will _____ by $_____, their lending

    activities will _____, interest rates will _____ and the money

    supply will _____ by $_____. If the

    bonds are sold to the chartered banks the money supply will _____.

7. An increase in the Central Bank Rate is generally considered to be an indication

    that monetary policy is becoming _____.

8. To stimulate economic recovery, the Bank of Canada could adopt a(n)

    _____ money policy which would _____ the money supply,

    which would tend to _____ interest rates.

9. The action taken by the Bank of Canada, as identified in the previous question,

    could be accomplished by (selling/buying) bonds in the open market,

    (raising/lowering) the Bank Rate, or by transferring Government of Canada

    deposits (into/out of) the chartered banks.

10. During a recession, the appropriate monetary and fiscal policies are

    (a)   tight money and a budget surplus.

    (b)   tight money and a budget deficit.

    (c)   easy money and a budget surplus.

    (d)   easy money and a budget deficit.

11. During a period of inflation, the appropriate monetary and fiscal policies are

    (a)   tight money and a budget deficit.

    (b)   tight money and a budget surplus.

    (c)   easy money and a budget deficit.

    (d)   easy money and a budget surplus.

12. A tight money policy tends to have a particularly severe effect on the sales of

    (a)   the food industry.

    (b)   the housing industry.

    (c)   the gasoline industry.

    (d)   the clothing industry.

(e)   the entertainment industry.

13.   Suppose the federal government finances large budget deficits by selling government bonds to the Bank of Canada. The Bank of Canada will pay the federal government for these bonds by _____.

14.   As a result of the situation described in the previous question, the nation's money supply will _____, and the rate of inflation will _____. However, if a budget deficit is financed by selling bonds to the public the nation's money supply will _____ and the rate of inflation will _____.

15.   During the first half of the 1970s,

(a)   Canada's money supply grew relatively slowly, causing an economic slowdown.

(b)   monetary policy was primarily concerned with restraining inflation.

(c)   (a) and (b) above.

(d)   Canada's money supply increased unusually rapidly, generating severe inflation.

(e)   none of the above.

16.   State whether each of the following statements concerning the monetary situation in Canada since the mid-1970s is TRUE or FALSE.

_____ (a)   There has been widespread agreement on the importance of controlling the growth of the money supply.

_____ (b)   The Bank of Canada undertook from 1975 to 1982 to keep the growth of the money supply within publicly announced limits.

_____ (c)   Canada's monetary policy has been more influenced by "monetarism" than it was earlier in the decade.

_____ (d)   The Bank of Canada's policies have contributed to high interest rates.

_____ (e)   The Bank of Canada used M1 as the official measure of the money supply from 1975 to 1982.

17.   "Fiscal policy" refers to:

(a)   the printing of additional money during economic recessions.

(b)　the use of government expenditures and tax revenues to influence the performance of the economy.

(c)　the use of budget deficits to combat recessions.

(d)　the use of budget surpluses to combat inflation.

(e)　(b) and (c) and (d) together.

18.　When there is a government budget deficit, government spending is

(a)　rising.

(b)　less than tax revenues.

(c)　equal to tax revenues.

(d)　greater than tax revenues.

(e)　falling.

19.　A government budget deficit will tend to _____ aggregate demand, GDP and total incomes.

20.　When there is a government budget surplus, government spending is

(a)　falling.

(b)　greater than tax revenues.

(c)　rising.

(d)　equal to tax revenues.

(e)　less than tax revenues.

21.　A government budget surplus will tend to _____ incomes.

22.　When government's budget is balanced, government spending is

(a)　less than tax revenues.

(b)　equal to tax revenues.

(c)　rising.

(d)　greater than tax revenues.

(e)　falling.

23.　A balanced government budget will have a _____ effect on GDP and total incomes.

24.　Which of the following policies should be used by the federal government during an economic recession?

_____ (a)   Postponement of a program aimed at encouraging provincial highway construction.

_____ (b)   Increases in social welfare payments to individuals.

_____ (c)   Reduction of subsidies to farmers and other forms of transfer payments (such as unemployment insurance).

_____ (d)   Reduction of federal tax rates on personal and corporate income.

_____ (e)   Controls on government spending designed to produce a federal budget surplus.

_____ (f)   Increased depreciation allowances (capital cost allowances) for corporations.

_____ (g)   Increases in government spending on public works.

25. During an economic recession, the federal budget should be

(a)   set so that government spending is less than tax revenues.

(b)   set so that government spending equals tax revenues.

(c)   designed to enable the government to reduce the National Debt.

(d)   set so that government spending is greater than tax revenues.

(e)   reduced.

26. Explain briefly how "counter cyclical fiscal policy" can be used to reduce the level of economic fluctuations:

_____

_____

_____

27. Which of the following are examples of automatic stabilizers?

_____ (a)   the Employment Insurance Plan.

_____ (b)   increased hiring of unemployed people by various government departments.

_____ (c)   public works projects such as roads and parks construction.

_____ (d)   the Personal Income Tax system.

28. If the size of the multiplier is 1.6 and government spending is increased by $70 million (without any change in taxes), GDP will _____.

29. Which of the following is generally considered to be the most appropriate way to finance federal budget deficits?

   (a) Print as much money as necessary to finance the deficit.

   (b) Borrow the money by selling bonds.

   (c) Borrow the money from the World Bank.

   (d) Borrow from other nations.

   (e) None of the above.

30. If the government finances budget deficits by excessive printing of more money, the result will be _____

   _____

   _____

31. The "National Debt" is defined as _____

   _____

32. How is the National Debt related to federal government budget deficits?

   _____

   _____

   _____

33. Which of the following are considered to be legitimate economic reasons for government borrowing?

   _____ (a) to finance budget deficits for the purpose of combatting economic recessions.

   _____ (b) to finance the government's operating expenses, such as payroll.

   _____ (c) to finance the deficits of Crown corporations such as the Post Office.

   _____ (d) to finance production of transportation facilities, such as roads, airports, and harbours.

   _____ (e) to finance wartime: government expenditures.

34. State whether each of the following statements concerning government budget deficits and the National Debt is TRUE or FALSE.

   _____ (a) Government budget deficits and debt are evidence of economic mismanagement on the part of the government.

_____ (b)   The National Debt need never be paid off.

_____ (c)   Interest payments on government debt represent a heavy burden on Canadians as a group.

_____ (d)   Budget deficits are proof of inefficiency in the operation of government departments and services.

_____ (e)   Excessive budget deficits can contribute to inflation.

_____ (f)   Budget deficits and government debt inevitably impose economic burdens on future generations.

_____ (g)   The National Debt is owed mainly to Canadians.

_____ (h)   Excessive budget deficits can depress capital investment and economic growth.

_____ (i)   The National Debt as a percentage of GDP has risen steadily since 1950.

_____ (j)   Government budget deficits are not comparable to business losses.

_____ (k)   Large government budget deficits can cause higher interest rates.

35.   As a consequence of massive federal deficits during the 1980s, capital investment by business may be depressed due to:

(1)   _____

       _____

(2)   _____

       _____

36.   The "crowding out" of capital investment by government borrowing to pay for current expenses means that

(a)   present generations enjoy greater consumption, but at the expense of future generations.

(b)   present generations are impoverished as interest charges on the National Debt escalate.

(c)   future generations will be better off, as investment opportunities will be greater.

(d)   neither present nor future generations can suffer any economic consequences.

37. The impact of a rising proportion of our National Debt being held by foreigners is that

    (a)   this represents a rising external burden on Canada's economy.

    (b)   future generations will be burdened by higher interest payments.

    (c)   future generations will be burdened by having to pay off the foreign debt.

    (d)   all of the above.

38. The large federal government deficits of the mid-1980s

    (a)   resulted in less flexibility in government actions to reduce unemployment.

    (b)   gave rise to concerns that severe inflation could result

    (c)   increased the value of the Canadian dollar.

    (d)   (a) and (b) above.

39. Higher federal government deficits exert an (upward, downward) influence on interest rates, since the federal government's consequent borrowing will (increase, decrease) the demand for money. In turn, the (higher, lower) interest rates will cause a(n) (increase, decrease) in the size of the government's deficit, since interest charges are now a (major, minor) budget item. If the government has to increase its borrowing in order to finance rising interest costs, the result can be compared to a (compound, simple) interest calculation.

40. Fill in the appropriate policy actions for government during:

Recessions	**Periods of boom/inflation**
(a) Monetary Policy:	**(a) Monetary Policy:**
An "_____"	An "_____"
policy which would cause	policy which would cause
interest rates to _____.	interest rates to _____.
(b) Fiscal Policy	**(b) Fiscal Policy**
A government budget	A government budget
_____, with gov't	_____, with gov't
spending _____	spending _____
its tax revenues.	its tax revenues.
(c) How these Policies Work:	**(c) How these Policies Work:**
(a) and (b) will shorten the	(a) and (b) will reduce the

recession by _____
_____ .

rate of inflation by _____
_____ .

(d) Side-Effects of Policies:

If used too strongly, the

policies in (a) and (b) may

cause _____

if they _____

_____ .

(d) Side-Effects of Policies:

The policies in (a) and (b)

will cause _____

_____ ,

because they _____

_____ .

41.   On the expenditure side, federal government deficit reduction is very difficult

since:

(1)   _____ and

(2)   _____

42.   The generally accepted view of government deficits is that

(a)   it would be more desirable for governments to balance their budget at all

times.

(b)   they should be reduced when the country enters into a recession.

(c)   they are an appropriate policy for dealing with economic recession.

(d)   their presence indicates fiscal irresponsibility by governments.

43.   Match the following terms in the first column with the definitions in the second

column.

	Treasury Bill	A	The rate of interest charged by lenders to their most creditworthy borrowers.
	Easy Money Policy	B	The use of govt. spending and taxes to influence the level of aggregate demand and thus the performance of the economy
	Prime Rate	C	Short term federal government promissory notes that are sold at weekly auctions.
	Tight Money Policy	D	Monetary policy directed towards making interest rates lower in order to Stimulate aggregate demand
	Fiscal Policy	E	Government spending and taxation programs that have the effect of automatically supporting aggregate demand during recessions and depressing aggregate demand during periods of boom/inflation.

Automatic Stabalizer	F	Monetary policy directed toward making interest rates higher in order to slow the growth of aggregate demand
Budget Deficit	G	A government budget in which tax revenues and expenditures are equal.
Balanced Budget	H	A government budget in which expenditures exceed tax revenues

Macro Chapter 8

Perspectives on Macroeconomic Policy

This chapter deals with the critical economic problem of unemployment and the effectiveness of government policies in combating this problem. Causes and characteristics of the five types of unemployment are examined, as is the concept of full employment.

Monetary and fiscal policies to increase aggregate demand may reduce unemployment if there is capacity available in the economy. However, if the economy is at or close to full capacity these policies may lead to an increase in inflation. Time lags and international forces can also limit the effectiveness of government action.

General Learning Objective

Examine briefly the nature and causes of unemployment in Canada and discuss the practical problems and limitations faced by government in applying monetary and fiscal policy.

Specific Learning Objectives

		Self-Test Reference
1.	Recognize the types of unemployment	#1-7
2.	Examine the effects of monetary and fiscal policy	#8-12
3.	Define full employment and the employment to population ratio	#13,14
4.	Summarize policies to reduce unemployment	#15
5.	Identify time lags that effect government policy	#16, 17
6.	Explain international limitations on government policy	#18-21
7.	Consider Canada's economic goals	#22-24
8.	Recognize the key terms used in this chapter	#25

Self-Test

1. Better training of the labour force may decrease _____ unemployment.

2. Your age and the area of Canada in which you live are two major factors affecting your chances of being unemployed, in that _____

    _____

    _____

    _____

    _____

3. "Higher productivity (output per worker) can increase unemployment."
    Comment: _____

    _____

    _____

    _____

4. Two reasons technology may increase employment _____

    _____ .

5. One reason technology may decrease employment is _____

    _____ .

6. "Voluntary unemployment"

    (a) exists when people volunteer for work but no employer can be found who is willing to hire them.

    (b) indicates a situation where people choose not to take jobs which are available.

    (c) is reduced through the combination of employment insurance and the existing tax system.

    (d) has added at least five percentage points to the unemployment rate, according to most economists.

7. Which of the following is NOT considered to have been a factor generating "voluntary unemployment"?

    (a) Increased selectivity of job-seekers.

(b)   The more accessible and more attractive employment insurance benefits available after 1971.

(c)   Increased laziness on the part of Canadian workers.

(d)   An increase in the number of secondary income-earners (such as young people and married women) in the labour force.

(e)   An increased tendency of people to remain unemployed longer than really necessary before finding jobs.

8.   If there is very high unemployment in the economy and aggregate demand increases,

(a)   real output, employment, and prices will all rise rapidly.

(b)   real output and employment will rise rapidly, and there will be little or no increase in prices.

(c)   real output and employment will rise, and prices will fail.

(d)   real output, employment, and prices will all fall.

(e)   none of the above.

9.   If the economy is near, but not yet at, full employment (or capacity production) and aggregate demand increases, real output and employment will rise (more/less) rapidly, and prices will rise (more/less) rapidly than in the previous question.

10.   If the economy is at full employment (or capacity production) and aggregate demand increases,

(a)   real output and employment will rise less rapidly than before capacity production was reached, and prices will stabilize.

(b)   real output, employment and prices will all stabilize.

(c)   real output and employment will fall, but prices will rise rapidly.

(d)   real output and employment will not increase further, but prices will rise rapidly.

(e)   none of the above.

11.   An economic trade-off is involved whenever government decides to _____

    _____

    _____

12.   Government policies to counter unemployment may not be implemented because

    of the fear of _____.

13.   Full employment is defined as _____

    _____

14.   What does Canada's employment to population ratio show?

    _____

15.   (a)   What measures might be taken to combat unemployment?

    _____

    _____

    _____

    _____

    (b)   Explain how each of the above will reduce structural unemployment.

    _____

    _____

    _____

    _____

16.   Monetary and fiscal policies do not affect the economy as quickly as we would

    like. Name and explain briefly each of the three "time lags" which slow the

    response of the economy to these policies.

    (a)   _____

    _____

    _____

    (b)   _____

    _____

    _____

    (c)   _____

    _____

    _____

17. State whether each of the following statements regarding government policies is **TRUE** or **FALSE**.

_____ (a)   Their effects are always felt immediately.

_____ (b)   They benefit from accurate economic forecasts.

_____ (c)   They should address actual, not expected, economic conditions.

_____ (d)   They often respond more to short-term political considerations than long-term economic considerations.

_____ (e)   It may take 1-2 years for an effect to be felt.

_____ (f)   Policy makers should direct their actions towards changing economic conditions.

18. Explain the main international limitation on Canadian monetary policy.

_____

_____

_____

19. State whether each of the following would be a likely result if Canadian interest rates were not kept higher than US interest rates.

_____ (a)   Canadians' living standards would be reduced.

_____ (b)   There would be no significant effect on Canada economically, because Canadian interest rates are not related to US rates.

_____ (c)   Capital flows from the USA to Canada would be reduced.

_____ (d)   Capital investment in Canada would tend to be depressed by a lack of funds.

_____ (e)   The international value of the Canadian dollar (compared to the US dollar) would fall.

20. If Canada's rate of inflation significantly exceeded the USA's rate of inflation for long, which of the following would be likely to happen?

_____ (a)   Canada's exports to the USA would decrease.

_____ (b)   Canadians would travel less to the USA.

_____ (c)   Canada's imports from the USA would increase.

_____ (d)   Unemployment in Canada would increase.

21. Explain the main limitation on Canadian fiscal policy.

    _____

    _____

    _____

22. State the three major goals of an economic system.

    (a) _____

    (b) _____

    (c) _____

23. State which one of the three goals in the previous question conflicts with the other two goals. _____

24. The conflict referred to in the previous question exists because _____

    _____

    _____

25. Match the following terms in the first column with the definitions in the second column.

	Employment to Population Ratio	A	Unemployment that is caused by periodic cyclical weaknesses in aggregate demand associated with recessions
	Capacity output	B	A government budget in which tax revenues exceed tax expenditures.
	Budget Surplus	C	The maximum real output which the economy is capable producing in any given year.
	Recognition Lag	D	The percentage of the working age population that is employed.
	Time Lag	E	The lowest rate of unemployment that can be achieved without generating unacceptable inflation in the economy.
	Impact Lag	F	Period of time for economic policy to effect inflation or unemployment
	Cyclical Unemployment	G	The time between the existence of a problem and the clear recognition of it by economic policy –makers.
	Policy Lag	H	Period of time before government economic policy changes can be put in place.
	Full employment	I	Period of time it takes for economic policies to take effect

Macro Chapter 9

INTERNATIONAL TRADE

The matters covered in this chapter are of particular importance to Canada, which exports (and imports) roughly 35-40% of its GDP. The theory of international trade is quite simple: free trade promotes specialization, efficiency and therefore prosperity. In practice, however, nations tend to place barriers in the way of free trade for various reasons. For over a century, Canada has used tariffs to protect and stimulate the development of the nation's manufacturing sector. The positive results of this policy are that Canada now has a larger manufacturing sector and more diversified economy than would have existed otherwise. On the other hand, this manufacturing sector consists largely of small-scale "branch plants" of foreign firms which are not very efficient and are therefore vulnerable to foreign competition and must be subsidized by continuing protection against imports.

A major policy problem facing Canada is how to increase the international competitiveness of Canadian industry in the future. This goal has become more attainable now in light of NAFTA, the free trade agreement with the United States and Mexico. Canadian manufacturers will be under increasing competitive pressure to use the most cost-efficient methods of production.

The conclusion of this chapter is that the long-run benefits of freer trade outweigh the costs. It is an important conclusion and one too easily forgotten by politicians and policy makers in the past.

General Learning Objective

Establish the economic costs and benefits of international free trade.

Specific Learning Objectives

		Self-Test Reference
1.	Examine the facts regarding Canada's trade with other nations	#1, 2
2.	Identify tariffs and non-tariff barriers	#3, 4
3.	Consider the benefits of specializing productive activities	#5-9
4.	Demonstrate the possible gains in productivity in the light of high wages	#10
5.	Examine the arguments for protection	#11-13
6.	Assess the economic effects of the import tariff	#14-19
7.	Identify the non-tariff barriers to trade	#20
8.	Consider policies to alleviate the costs of freer trade	#21
9.	Consider the effects of globalization on Canada	#22. 23
10.	Recognize the terms used in this chapter	#24

Self-Test

1. Canada's dependence on exports is

    (a)   high by international standards

    (b)   low by international standards

    (c)   average by international standards

2. As of 1998 which country or bloc of countries accounted for the vast majority of Canada's exports and imports?

    (a)   Japan

    (b)   The United States

    (c)   Europe

    (d)   China

    (e)   The United Kingdom

3. A tariff is a tax that

    (a)   lowers the price of domestic goods

    (b)   raises the price of domestic goods

    (c)   lowers the price of foreign goods

(d)   raises the price of foreign goods

(e)   none of the above

4.   List six non-tariff barriers.

(a)   _____

(b)   _____

(c)   _____

(d)   _____

(e)   _____

(f)   _____

5.   If Canada is 20% more efficient at producing telecommunication equipment and 15% more efficient at producing plastics than their trading partners, Canada should specialize in the production and export of _____. This decision fits with the theory of _____.

6.   A trend toward freer international trade would represent

(a)   a threat to all sectors of the Canadian economy.

(b)   a threat to some sectors of the Canadian economy.

(c)   an opportunity for some sectors of the Canadian economy.

(d)   an opportunity for all sectors of the Canadian economy.

(e)   (b) and (c) together.

7.   To demonstrate the advantages of international trade, number the following in the order that they are expected to occur.

_____ (a)   The nation realizes increased efficiencies of production reflected in lower per unit costs.

_____ (b)   Specialization occurs.

_____ (c)   The nation considers what they do best.

_____ (d)   The nation realizes an improved standard of living.

8.   Freer trade promotes higher productivity in three ways. They are _____, _____ and _____.

9.   The specialization in the production of goods that a country is efficient at producing is called _____

10.   A western Canadian company using local poplar wood produces disposable unfinished chopsticks using the most advanced equipment. A major portion of the output is exported to Asian countries. The average hourly output is 3000 chopsticks and the hourly costs are $90.

A Chinese company using less capital but more labour produces an equivalent product. In China, hourly production is 200 chopsticks and hourly costs are $10.

(a)   Complete the following chart.

	Canadian Firm	Chinese Firm
Hourly costs	_____	_____
Hourly output	_____	_____
Cost per chopstick	_____	_____

(b)   How do we measure productive efficiency in this example?

_____

(c)   What factor of production might account for the difference in efficiency?

_____

(d)   Determine the total cost in each country for an order for 2 million chopsticks. _____

11.   "The products of North American manufacturers cannot compete in price with the products of low-wage nations such as Taiwan and Hong Kong."

State whether the above statement is TRUE or FALSE, and explain the reason for your answer.

_____

_____

_____

12.   "As a generality, it is true that Canadian producers favour protective tariffs."
Is this statement TRUE or FALSE? Why? _____

_____

_____

_____

13.   In the "infant industry" argument for protective tariffs, it usually happens that

(a)   the protected industry matures and becomes sufficiently competitive so that it no longer requires tariff protection.

(b)   the protected industries develop slowly, requiring tariff protection for much longer than was intended, perhaps indefinitely.

(c)   the tax revenues from tariffs make it possible for the government to reduce the overall tax burden on the Canadian public.

(d)   the protected industries often develop into leading exporters.

(e)   (a) and (d) together.

14.   The demand and supply schedules below represent the Canadian market for running shoes. The supply schedule is that of Canadian producers and the demand schedule indicates the desires of Canadian consumers.

Before international trade, the Canadian price is $50, with production and consumption at 100 000 units.

Now, assume an international price of $35 with no trade restrictions preventing Canadians from purchasing the identical international product.

Draw in a price of $35 on the graph.

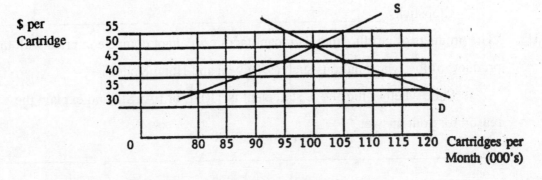

As a result of the lower priced imports, determine:

(a)   Canadians' planned purchases   _____

(b)   production by Canadian firms   _____

(c)   imports   _____

(d)   tariff revenues resulting from imports   _____

As a result of lobbying by Canadian producers of this product, the Canadian government levies a tariff of $10 per unit. The importers pass the tariff on to the consumer and the new market price is $45 per unit.

Draw the $45 price on the graph. Determine:

(e)   Canadian purchases   _____

(f)   production by Canadian firms   _____

(g)   imports   _____

(h)   tariff revenues resulting from imports   _____

(i)   From the following groups, determine who gains and who loses as a result
       of the imposition of the Canadian tariff. Why do they gain or lose?

Consumers _____

_____

Foreign Suppliers _____

_____

Canadian Importers _____

_____

Government _____

_____

Canadian Firms _____

_____

(j)   If Canadian producers are new in the business of running shoe production, is there
       a better way of providing some financial help?

_____

_____

15.   If Canada has an unemployment problem which it tries to solve by increasing
       tariffs on foreign imports so as to encourage Canadians to buy goods produced by
       Canadian workers instead, the most likely effect that this will have on
       employment in Canada is that

_____

_____

_____

16. Which one of the following statements is NOT true? A tariff on German widgets imported into Canada

  (a) will reduce the economic prosperity of the Canadian public.

  (b) will benefit the Canadian public in general.

  (c) will result in higher widget prices in Canada.

  (d) could result in fewer exports of Canadian products to Germany.

  (e) will benefit Canadian widget producers and their workers.

17. From the viewpoint of the economist, state whether each of the following is a reasonable argument in favour of placing tariffs on foreign goods imported into Canada.

  _____ (a) Tariffs protect the jobs of Canadians, and reduce unemployment.

  _____ (b) Tariffs protect Canada against foreign competition.

  _____ (c) Tariffs can assist in industrial development by getting "infant industries" established, whereas without tariffs they might not have survived.

  _____ (d) Tariffs can encourage foreign manufacturers to establish branch plants in Canada, thus generating industrial development.

  _____ (e) Several Canadian industries are experiencing strong competition from foreign producers, and are requesting that the government provide them with tariff protection.

  _____ (f) Tariffs can help to diversify the economy, so that it is not dependent upon a few resource industries alone, but rather has manufacturing industries as well.

  _____ (g) Tariffs (on foreign goods) will reduce the tax burden on the Canadian public.

  _____ (h) Tariffs prevent other nations from taking money out of Canada.

18. Tariffs and other trade restrictions have three negative effects on productivity and living standards. They are _____

_____

_____

19.   Label the following **True** or **False**.

_____ (a)   Tariffs help all industries in an economy.

_____ (b)   Free trade will move jobs to foreign countries.

_____ (c)   Firms always move to countries that have the lowest wages for workers.

_____ (d)   Tariffs can offer protection to infant industries in a country.

20.   Identify the non-tariff barriers to trade in the following list.

(a)   A duty is levied on the value of potatoes imported from the USA.

(b)   During the early 1980s, Canadian customs authorities delayed the processing of imported cars by a strict enforcement of paper work.

(c)   A quota is imposed on imports of childrens' clothing.

(d)   The provincial government provides subsidies for Canadian lumber exporters.

(e)   Tax incentives are granted to selected Canadian exporters.

21.   Name at least three ways in which governments could ease the negative effects of tariff reductions on protected Canadian industries.

(a)   _____

(b)   _____

(c)   _____

22.   Globalization would be most helpful to which of the following industries?

(a)   An efficient industry in a country with a small domestic market.

(b)   A heavily subsidized industry in a country with a small domestic market.

(c)   An efficient industry in a country with a large domestic market.

(d)   A heavily subsidized industry in a country with a large domestic market.

23.   The trend of globalization has the following effects on Canada:

(a)   stronger competition

(b)   lower costs to the Canadian consumer

(c)   growing markets for Canadian firms.

(d)   increased pressure on Canadians to reduce tariffs and other trade barriers.

(e)   all of the above.

24.   Match the terms on the left with definitions on the right

	Subsidy	A.	Canada limits imports of children's footwear.
	Bureaucratic procedure	B.	Coca-Cola Canada Ltd.
	Tariff	C.	Canada decides to produce and export steel in lieu of clothing production.
	Import quota	D.	Canadian customs officials enforce documentation requirements slowing down the importation of Japanese autos.
	Branch plant	E.	The import tax levied on foreign wines.
	Comparative advantage theory	F.	Turkey producers receive 15 cents per kilogram to offset production costs.
	Globalization	G.	More trade and investment conducted between countries.

Macro Chapter 10

THE CANADIAN DOLLAR IN FOREIGN EXCHANGE MARKETS

There are two basic concepts in this chapter:

(a)   foreign exchange markets, and

(b)   the international Balance of Payments of a nation.

Regarding (a), nations' currencies are bought and sold in markets, in which demand and supply cause their prices in terms of each other (exchange rates) to fluctuate. Regarding (b), a nation's international financial transactions can be summarized into its Balance of Payments, which shows all of that nation's receipts from and payments to other nations.

The interactions between the exchange rate and the Balance of Payments can be quite complex, but are essentially two-way:

(a)   the Balance of Payments influences the exchange rate: Balance of Payments deficits cause the exchange rate to fall, while surpluses cause the exchange rate to rise.

(b)   the exchange rate influences the Balance of Payments: a decline in the exchange rate increases a nation's receipts and reduces its payments, while a rise in the exchange rate increases a nation's payments and reduces its receipts.

When these international economic forces are allowed to work themselves out freely in markets, a "floating" exchange rate system is said to be in effect. Under a floating exchange rate system, the international price of a nation's currency will rise and fall in response to changes in the demand for and supply of it, in exports and imports, and in the flows of capital into and out of that nation. However, governments often do not allow their exchange rates to float freely; rather, many governments (including Canada's) practise what is called a "dirty float," in which they influence their exchange rates. This is done mainly through purchases or sales of Canadian dollars in foreign exchange markets by the Bank of Canada. If the Bank of Canada buys Canadian dollars, the exchange rate tends to rise: such a policy would depress import prices and restrain inflation, but also would depress exports and thus add to unemployment. If the Bank of Canada sells Canadian dollars, the exchange rate tends to decline: this would increase exports and reduce unemployment, but at the expense of higher import prices and more inflation.

Thus, exchange rate policy, like monetary and fiscal policy, involves trade-offs between the goals of full employment and stable prices, with lower exchange rates contributing to one and higher exchange rates contributing to the other. As with monetary and fiscal policy, the government tries to achieve a balance between these conflicting policy goals.

In the mid-1970s, the Canadian dollar traded at par with the American dollar. Since that time, depreciating forces have forced a decline in Canada's exchange rate, which has reduced Canadians' living standards but increased employment by making Canadian industry more internationally competitive. For several years during the mid-1970s, Canadians' incomes rose too fast for productivity, forcing production costs out of line with our competitors'. The decline in Canada's exchange rate was therefore quite similar to the nation's work force taking an international pay cut in exchange for improved job security, somewhat like auto workers did in the early 1980s, but on a grand scale.

The Canadian dollar has come under attack by foreign holders several times during the 1980s. The most serious selling of our dollar occurred in early 1986 as the price fell below the benchmark $.70 American. This prompted the Bank of Canada to embark on a massive buying of Canadian dollars and selling of foreign currencies. It also necessitated a substantial rise in our short-term interest rates at a time when lower rates were warranted to sustain the economic expansion and enhance employment. This latter crisis is an excellent example of the necessary trade-offs involved in public policy — especially the trade-off of higher interest rates to gain an appreciated currency.

The Canadian dollar gained strength as of 1988, reflecting the large inflows of foreign capital in our debt and equity markets. This was more than enough to offset our declining merchandise balance and Canada's increasing deficit on tourism and investment income flows. The result was a Canadian dollar in the range of $.85 Am. over 1989 and 1990.

By 1993, the Canadian dollar had again depreciated to the $.71 American level. It appears that Canada's increased indebtedness to foreigners was a primary reason. Like all excessive debts, the costs of servicing began to overcome the benefits of the loan.

By early 1998 the Canadian dollar was again below the benchmark $.70 American but the Bank of Canada did not intervene. As a result of our increasing dependence on foreign capital inflows to cover the increased interest payments on the foreign debt, the Bank of Canada now has less control over domestic monetary policy.

General Learning Objective

Explain the operation of foreign exchange markets and interpret a nation's International Balance of Payments statement.

Specific Learning Objectives

		Self-Test Reference
1.	Define the "exchange rate"	#1-3
2.	Determine the factors that affect the foreign exchange value of the Canadian dollar	#4
3.	Explain the concept of a "floating" exchange rate	#5, 6
4.	Analyze a Balance of Payments statement	#7-10c
5.	Define "dirty float"	#10d-11

6.   Identify the costs and benefits of a depreciating or appreciating

Canadian dollar   #12-20

7.   Consider the activity of foreign exchange speculators   #21

8.   Analyze long-run changes in Balance of Payments statements since 1970   #22-26

9.   Consider limiting and protective factors that act on currencies   #27-28

10.   Recognize the key terms used in this chapter   #29

Self-Test

1.   The foreign exchange rate is defined as _____.

2.   If $1 Canadian = $.8585 American; then $1 American = _____Canadian.

3.   If 1 pound Sterling = $1.9121 Canadian; then $1 Canadian =_____pounds

Sterling.

4.   (a)   If foreign businesses increase the flow of investment capital into Canada

over last year's levels with other factors constant, this will tend to cause

the international value of the Canadian dollar to

_____.

(b)   If Canadian imports of foreign automobiles increase over the level of the

previous year with other factors constant, this will tend to cause the

international value of the Canadian dollar to

_____.

(c)   If the Canadian subsidiaries of American corporations increase the amount

of dividends which they pay to their US-based parent companies with

other factors constant, the international value of the Canadian dollar would

tend to _____.

(d)   An increase in the number of immigrants coming to Canada (and bringing

funds with them) would tend to cause the international value of the

Canadian dollar to _____.

(e)   If many Canadians travel abroad to the World Bejuniaberry Festival in the

Duchy of Grand Fenwick, this would tend to cause the international value

of the Canadian dollar to _____.

(f)   An increase in Canadian short-term interest rates relative to equivalent American interest rates tends to cause the international value of the Canadian dollar to _____.

(g)   For the above answers (a) through (f), distinguish between a depreciation (D) of the Canadian dollar and an appreciation (A).

5.   If Canada is operating on a floating exchange rate system, the international value of the Canadian dollar will

(a)   remain stable (at one fixed level as decided by international agreement).

(b)   float steadily upwards in relation to other currencies.

(c)   gradually decline in relation to other currencies.

(d)   rise and fall as the supply of and demand for Canadian dollars in international money markets change.

(e)   none of the above.

6.   Suppose that Canada is operating on a floating exchange rate system and that Canada has a Balance of Payments surplus. In these circumstances, the international value of the Canadian dollar would tend to

_____.

7.   Classify each of the following transactions as a Canadian "receipt" or "payment."

(a)   Foreign tourists spend money in Canada.

(b)   Canada imports Japanese automobiles.

(c)   Canadian companies build plants in the USA.

(d)   Canadian subsidiaries of foreign companies pay dividends to their parent companies in Europe.

(e)   Foreign firms buy controlling interest in Canadian companies.

(f)   Ontario Hydro pays interest to US bondholders.

(g)   Canadians visit Disney World in Florida.

(h)   B.C. Hydro borrows $500 million in New York.

8.   (a)   If Canada's receipts exceed payments, Canada has a Balance of Payments

_____.

(b)   If Canada's payments exceed receipts, Canada has a Balance of Payments

_____.

(c)   Balance of Payments deficits tend to (depreciate/appreciate) the Canadian dollar, whereas a balance of payments surplus tends to _____ the dollar. The latter results from the increased (demand/supply) for our currency.

9.   A HYPOTHETICAL SUMMARY OF CANADA'S BALANCE OF PAYMENTS

(Millions of Dollars)

CURRENT ACCOUNT	RECEIPTS	PAYMENTS	BALANCE
Merchandise	$900	$1200	– $300
Travel	150	50	+ 100
Interest and Dividends	150	350	– 200
Government Contributions	—	100	– 100
BALANCE ON CURRENT ACCOUNT	$1200	$1700	– $500
CAPITAL ACCOUNT			
Capital Movements	$600	$ 200	+$400
BALANCE ON CAPITAL ACCOUNT	$600	$ 200	+$400
OVERALL BALANCE (Current and Capital Accounts)			– $100

(a)   Based on the Balance of Payments statement, are the following **TRUE** or **FALSE**?

_____ (i)   Canada sold more merchandise internationally than it bought.

_____ (ii)   Foreign tourists spent more money in Canada than Canadian tourists spent in foreign countries.

_____ (iii)   Canada received more in interest and dividends than were paid out of Canada.

_____ (iv)   Canada gave foreign aid to other nations.

_____ (v)   Canadian investment in foreign countries exceeded foreign investment in Canada.

(b)   Canada had a Balance of Payments

_____.

(c)   If the price of the Canadian dollar were allowed to "float" freely, it would tend to _____.

(d)   One group within Canada which would benefit economically from the change in the price of the Canadian dollar in (c) above would be

_____ because _____

_____

_____

(e)   The group(s) within Canada that would be hurt economically by this change in the price of the Canadian dollar would be _____,

because _____

_____

_____

10.   There are two important facts about the current account of the Canadian Balance of Payments. Because of our long Canadian winters, increasing numbers of Canadians take winter holidays in foreign countries. Secondly, Canadians pay increasing amounts of interest and dividends to foreigners who have both invested in Canada and loaned funds to Canadians.

How does the above affect:

(a)   The current account of Canada's Balance of Payments? _____

_____

_____

(b)   The foreign exchange price of the Canadian dollar assuming a purely floating exchange rate? _____

(c)   The prices of Canadian imports, as a result of (b)? _____.

(d)   If the Bank of Canada desires an appreciation of the Canadian dollar, it could:

        (i) _____

        (ii) _____

(e)   Assuming floating exchange rates, the activity of the Bank of Canada in (d) is referred to as a _____

_____

251

11.   Under a dirty float, the government

    (a)   allows the international value of its currency to fluctuate freely with supply and demand.

    (b)   manipulates the international value of its currency contrary to the wishes of its trading partners.

    (c)   prevents any fluctuations in the international value of its currency.

    (d)   intervenes in foreign exchange markets to moderate fluctuations in the international value of its currency.

    (e)   permits the international value of its currency to float, but prevents speculative purchases and sales of the currency which could cause its value to fluctuate.

12.   If the international value of the Canadian dollar were to decline unusually rapidly, there would be a risk of

    (a)   more severe inflation in Canada.

    (b)   more severe competition from foreign manufacturers.

    (c)   less severe competition from foreign manufacturers.

    (d)   (a) and (b) above.

    (e)   (a) and (c) above.

13.   If the international value of the Canadian dollar were to rise unusually rapidly, there would be a risk of

    (a)   more severe inflation in Canada.

    (b)   more severe competition from foreign manufacturers.

    (c)   an increase in unemployment in Canada.

    (d)   (b) and (c) above.

    (e)   none of the above.

14.   If the international value of the Canadian dollar were under downward pressure which the Canadian government wished to resist, the Bank of Canada could _____ interest rates in Canada.

15.   If the Bank of Canada takes steps to increase the international value of the Canadian dollar, unemployment will _____ since export sales decrease, and inflation is likely to decrease since imported goods cost _____ .

16. If the Canadian government attempted to maintain the international value of the Canadian dollar far above its equilibrium level,

    (a) Canada would deplete its foreign exchange reserves.

    (b) over the longer run, the international value of the Canadian dollar would eventually fall to a more realistic level.

    (c) (a) and (b) above.

    (d) the result would be large increases in Canada's foreign exchange reserves.

    (e) there would be downward pressure on Canadian interest rates.

17. If the Canadian government attempted to maintain the international value of the Canadian dollar far below its equilibrium level,

    (a) the government would have to either "print" or borrow Canadian dollars on a large scale.

    (b) the Bank of Canada would buy Canadian dollars.

    (c) (a) and (b) above.

    (d) the Bank of Canada would have to hold Canadian interest rates at high levels relative to rates in other nations.

    (e) Canada's holdings of foreign exchange reserves would decline.

18. Higher budget deficits and lower interest rates is a formula for _____ (contractionary, expansionary) economic policy. The price of the Canadian dollar on foreign exchange markets is most likely to _____ (rise, fall). This makes Canadian goods _____ (more, less) expensive to foreigners. As a result, our export sales should _____ (increase, decrease).

19. Suppose that the Canadian dollar falls in price against the American dollar and the Bank of Canada takes action to increase the value of our currency.

    (a) Canadian pulp and paper executives are against the Bank of Canada intervention because _____

    _____

    _____

    (b) Canadian importers support the action of the Bank because _____

    _____

    _____

(c)   What is the Bank trying to accomplish? _____

_____

_____

20.   (a)   Dawna Rose is a Canadian automobile dealer who sells imported cars from Japan. In one year she imported 1000 new cars at an average price of 2.2 million yen per car. The exchange rate was 200 yen = $1 Canadian. The total Canadian dollar cost of cars for that year was $_____.

       (b)   The next year, the Canadian dollar depreciated against the yen to 140 yen = $1 Canadian. The total Canadian dollar cost to Dawna, who again imports 1000 cars at an average price of 2.2 million yen per car, was $_____.

       (c)   Based on the relative change in prices caused by the dollar depreciation, Canadians reduce their purchases of Japanese goods and services, whereas our exports to Japan increase.

              Thus, Canadian exports (increase/decrease) and our Japanese imports _____. This adjustment to our Balance of Payments resulting from floating exchange rates is referred to as the _____.

21.   State whether each of the following statements is TRUE or FALSE. If there were widespread rumours of a decline in the international value of the Canadian dollar, the actions of foreign exchange speculators would tend to

       _____ (a)   put an additional downward pressure on the international value of the Canadian dollar.

       _____ (b)   contribute to lower interest rates in Canada.

       _____ (c)   cause the Bank of Canada to buy Canadian dollars in foreign exchange markets.

       _____ (d)   make it more difficult for the Bank of Canada to stabilize the international value of the Canadian dollar.

       _____ (e)   contribute to lower prices of goods imported into Canada.

22.   State whether each of the following statements is TRUE or FALSE. By the early 1970s,

_____ (a)   Canada's current account deficits increased, but were financed increasingly by heavy borrowing abroad, mainly through bond issues.

_____ (b)   Canada's reliance on foreign capital decreased, as the current account deficit shrank, reducing Canada's need for foreign capital.

_____ (c)   Canada was widely believed to be maturing economically to the point where the nation's capital requirements could be financed within Canada.

23.   State whether each of the following would help to reduce Canada's need for foreign borrowing.

_____ (a)   Reductions in Canada's personal income tax.

_____ (b)   Reductions in the federal government's budget deficit.

_____ (c)   Increased exports of Canadian resources and other products.

_____ (d)   Reduced consumption by Canadians of foreign goods and services.

_____ (e)   Increased saving (and reduced consumption) by Canadians.

_____ (f)   Increases in federal government spending.

24.   The interest portion of the services deficit had grown substantially during the 1980s. The two possible reasons for this change are:

(1)   _____

(2)   _____

25.   (a).   Canada's massive debt to foreign lenders restricts the ability of the Bank of Canada to conduct monetary policy. For example, suppose the bank desires to pursue an expansionary policy to offset a pending recession.

The Bank becomes a net _____ (buyer, seller) of Treasury bills and as a result T-bill yields tend to _____ (increase, decrease). This change affects the differential between US and Canadian interest rates. Without a corresponding change to American rates, the _____ (American, Canadian) money market becomes more attractive to investors. This leads to net _____ (selling, buying) of Canadian dollar securities and a subsequent _____ (appreciation, depreciation) of the Canadian dollar.

(b)   If foreign holders of Canadian bonds panic and begin to sell their securities for foreign exchange, the Canadian dollar would depreciate in spite of actions by the Bank of Canada. Under these circumstances, control of the Canadian dollar price is impossible, since _____.

26.   As a result of the scenario presented in Question 25, Canadian living standards _____ (improve, stay the same, decline).

27.   A country with a very successful export industry would not be able to completely dominate the world with its products because

(a)   Its currency would depreciate, making its exports less expensive.

(b)   Its currency would appreciate, making its exports more expensive.

(d)   Its currency would depreciate, making its exports more expensive.

(e)   Its currency would appreciate, making its exports less expensive.

28.   Japan has had a very successful export industry, but because of Japan's success at exporting its exchange rates has appreciated. This is known as a _____ factor for Japanese industry.

29.   Match the terms on the left with the definitions on the right

30.

	Exchange Rate	A	Markets, conducted through banks in which currency is allowed to fluctuate freely with the supply of and demand for it
	Foreign Exchange Markets	B	The international price, or value, of a currency in foreign exchange markets.
	Balance of Payments	C	A situation in which a payments exceed its receipts.
	Current Account	D	Balance of payments items involving flows of investment funds (capital) both long-term and short term, between countries
	Capital Account	E	Balance of payments items relating to day to day transactions in goods and services, including interest and dividends.
	Hot Money	F	A situation in which government influences the exchange rate by purchases and sales of currencies in foreign exchange markets and changes in interest rates.

	Balance of Payments Deficit	G	Short-term funds that are used to speculate in currencies by being moved rapidly from currencies that are perceived as "weak" to currencies that are perceived as "stong"
	Floating Exchange Rate	H	Purchases and sales of currencies ,with the intention of earning profits on fluctuations in their values
	Dirty Float	I	A summary of all the nation's receipts and payments for a given year
	Foreign Exchange Speculation	J	A situation in which the international value of a currency is allowed to fluctuate freely with the supply of and demand for it.

Macro Chapter 11

THE GLOBAL ECONOMY

The basic concepts of international trade and finance have been established in Chapters 9-10. Chapter 11 uses these concepts to trace the evolution of the international monetary system over more than 50 years, from the extreme instability of the 1930s to the rigidity of the pegged system from 1945 to 1973, to the development of the dirty float after that. When the present situation is seen in historical perspective, it is apparent that nations are continuing the long search for an international monetary system that is neither too unstable nor too rigid to be workable and sustainable.

Chapter 11 also touches on a number of matters of international interest and importance such as the shift of world industrial power in favour of Japan and West Germany, currency devaluations, the role of gold in the international monetary system, gold speculation, the trials and tribulations of the US dollar and, finally, its devaluation.

We also consider the economic impact of the evolution of petro-dollars and the other pressures on currency prices. We look at the reasons for the strength of the American dollar during the first half of the 1980s and the causes of the American dollar depreciation during the latter half of the decade. Inevitably, the persistent federal government deficits and the Balance of Payments deficits played a role in the American dollar depreciation.

General Learning Objective

Explore the historical events from the 1930s to the present that had an impact on the evolution of the international monetary system.

Specific Learning Objectives

Self-Test

1. What two types of aggressive economic policies did countries resort to in the 1930's to attempt to reduce unemployment in their countries at the expense of their trading partners? _____

_____

2. The result of one country imposing high tariffs on another country was?

_____

3. What was the result of many countries devaluing their currencies?

_____

4. The 1930s could best be characterized as a period of
   (a) increased international trade and investment.
   (b) protectionism and a dramatic reduction in the amount of international trade.
   (c) booming economies around the world.
   (d) slow economic growth as the result of low tariff barriers.

5.   During the Great Depression of the 1930s

    (a)   nations agreed to peg exchange rates at agreed levels so as to encourage international trade.

    (b)   many nations sought to increase the value of their currency in order to increase the purchasing power of their consumers in international markets.

    (c)   exchange rates became very unstable as nations repeatedly devalued their currencies in attempts to gain competitive advantages over each other.

    (d)   the floating system of exchange rates worked quite successfully as currency values were able to respond quickly to the economic pressures of the Depression.

    (e)   none of the above.

6.   The situation referred to in the previous question caused international trade to (flourish/stagnate), making for a(n) (increase/decrease) in unemployment.

7.   The second half of the twentieth century saw the rise of

    (a)   Nationalism.

    (b)   Currency instability.

    (c)   Internationalism.

    (d)   Protectionism.

8.   The organization that was designed to decrease exchange rate instability is called?

    _____

9.   The organization designed to reduce tariff barriers and to promote international trade is called? _____

10.   While the organization in the previous question has successfully been able to reduce _____, there has been a substantial increase in

    _____.

11.   One of the problems that the GATT has faced since the 1980's has been a rise in

    (a)   protectionism.

    (b)   stock markets.

    (c)   oil prices.

    (d)   nationalism.

12. The WTO system encourages countries to

    (a)   resolve disputes on their own, if possible.

    (b)   increase tariff barriers in retaliation when there is a dispute.

    (c)   immediately take disputes to a neutral panel of experts.

    (d)   increase non-tariff barriers instead of tariffs.

13. The International Monetary Fund established a system of

    (a)   free floating exchange rates.

    (b)   international bond markets.

    (c)   pegged exchanged rates.

    (d)   savings and Loan buildings.

14. State whether each of the following is a way in which the International Monetary Fund would assist nations experiencing problems due to Balance of Payments deficits.

    _____ (a)   Asking other nations to reduce tariffs on that nation's goods.

    _____ (b)   Allowing that nation to increase its tariffs on foreign goods.

    _____ (c)   Lending that nation foreign currencies and gold.

    _____ (d)   Purchasing goods from that nation.

    _____ (e)   Purchasing that nation's currency.

15. (a)   In a pegged exchange rate system a country fighting downward pressure on its currency would quickly run out of foreign exchange reserves. What would the IMF do in this case?

    _____

    _____

    (b)   What would the conditions most likely be for a country that received help from the IMF?

    _____

    _____

16. In a pegged exchanged rate system governments would stabilize their exchange rates through _____

17. Why did the US dollar come to occupy a special place in the international monetary system? _____

_____

18. Immediately after World War II

   (a) the international monetary system fell into confusion due to the lack of a generally acceptable currency for use in international trade.

   (b) nations were unable to agree on which type of monetary system to use, so each nation acted according to its own preferences.

   (c) the nations of the world agreed to establish a single world currency to simplify international trade and finance.

   (d) the major trading nations of the world agreed to use a system of floating exchange rates.

   (e) the major trading nations agreed to set up a system of pegged exchange rates.

19. Which of the following are TRUE and which are FALSE regarding the international monetary system after World War II?

   _____ (a) The system was designed to prevent exchange rate fluctuations.

   _____ (b) There had to be an agreement to eliminate protectionist policies that destabilized international trade and investment.

   _____ (c) Governments would not intervene in foreign exchange markets to restore the "pegged" exchange rates.

   _____ (d) Unlike the concept of the "dirty float," the objective under a fixed exchange rate system is to prevent exchange rate fluctuations as opposed to moderating fluctuations.

20. For example, if Canada were operating on a pegged exchange rate system and had a Balance of Payments surplus, the international value of the Canadian dollar would tend to (rise/fall) and the Canadian government would have to (buy/sell) Canadian dollars and (buy/sell) foreign currencies and gold in order to maintain it at its pegged level.

21. Using the same choices as Question 20, if Canada were operating on a pegged exchange rate system and had a Balance of Payments deficit, the international value of the Canadian dollar would tend to _____, and the Canadian government would have to _____ Canadian dollars and _____ foreign currencies and gold in order to maintain it at its pegged level.

22. Which of the following best describes the position of the US dollar internationally during most of the postwar period (until about 1968)?

    (a) Considered to be a valuable asset for speculators to hold, not only because of its gold backing, but also because it was generally considered to be undervalued, and therefore likely to increase in value.

    (b) Not considered by most nations to be an acceptable medium of exchange in international trade because of its record of instability.

    (c) Less acceptable than gold to most nations for purposes of international trade, due to the fact that it could not actually be converted to gold.

    (d) The most commonly used currency in international trade and finance; the centre of the world's system of pegged exchange rates — largely due to the fact that it was backed by gold.

    (e) Widely used in international trade; the centre of the world's monetary system despite the fact that it had undergone two devaluations over the period.

23. Experience with the international monetary system established after World War II indicates that

    (a) exchange rates can be held at pegged levels for as long as governments possess the determination to do so.

    (b) the only really workable international monetary system is one that requires nations to peg their exchange rates rigidly and indefinitely.

    (c) exchange rates cannot be pegged at fixed levels for indefinite periods of time — sooner or later, some rates will change despite the pegged system.

    (d) the floating system established after World War II works extremely well in most circumstances.

    (e) (a) and (b) above.

24. Why is it not possible to peg the international values of all currencies
     indefinitely? _____

     _____

     _____

25. The process of a currency suddenly and sharply falling in value is?

     _____

26. How has the IMF evolved after the collapse of the pegged exchange rate system?

     _____

     _____

     _____

27. A tribunal of officials appointed by the WTO settles a trade dispute between
     Canada and France over Canadian Subsidies to fishers. This is an example of the
     WTO principle of

     (a)   observance, where nations that join the WTO agree to observe its
           negotiated terms.

     (b)   reciprocity.

     (c)   non-discrimination.

     (d)   impartial settlement of trade disputes.

28. The abandonment of the pegged exchange rate system has caused

     (a)   countries to return to manipulation of their currencies for short term gains.

     (b)   exchange rate instability.

     (c)   smooth sailing for all currencies.

     (d)   relative stability, but some fluctuations in exchange rates.

29. The difference between "floating" and "pegged" currency prices (exchange rates)
     is that:

     (a)   floating currency prices are free to move both up and down, while pegged
           currency prices are only permitted to move upwards.

     (b)   with pegged currency prices, governments act so as to prevent the prices
           of currencies from moving significantly upwards or downwards.

     (c)   only nations with Balance of Payments surpluses have floating exchange
           rates.

(d)   floating currency prices are usually higher than pegged currency prices.

(e)   pegged currency prices are considered to be appropriate for nations with Balance of Payments deficits.

30.   Under a pegged system, a country's level of foreign exchange reserves is (more/less) important relative to the reserve holdings under a floating rate system.

31.   Question 30 is true since under a pegged system the government (buys/sells) foreign exchange reserves and (buys/sells) its own currency if market forces push the value of the domestic currency below the pegged rate.

32.   In 1974 when the price of oil had increased to four or five times its previous levels $62 billion in funds flowed out of oil importing countries and into OPEC countries.

(a)   These funds were called _____

(b)   What was the effect on exchange rates of these flows of funds?

_____

_____

(c)   Would the effect have been worse if the pegged exchange rate system had been in place?

_____

_____

_____

33.   From the point of view of the United States the free trade agreement was a reaction to

(a)   The WTO.

(b)   APEC.

(c)   The European Union.

(d)   The IMF.

34.   What made the Asian financial crisis more important than a crisis that affected

        another country? _____

        _____

        _____

35.   What were the IMF conditions on granting loans to countries affected by the

        Asian financial crisis? _____

        _____

        _____

        _____

36.   By the middle of the 1990s which was the dominant force in international

        currency markets, capital flows or trade flows?

        _____

37. Match the terms on the left with the definitions on the right

	Trade War	A	Successor to the GATT as of 1995
	G.A.T.T	B	North American Trade Agreement between Canada United States and Mexico
	W.T.O.	C	An international agreement under which many nations following the 1947, negotiated reductions in tariffs in order to promote trade
	I.M.F.	D	A tariff imposed in response to a tariff or other restriction on imports imposed by another nation.
	Trading Blocks	E	A major free trade area comprised of most of the countries of Europe.
	Devaluation	F	Retaliatory escalation of trade barriers by nations against each others' exports
	Euro	G	Reduction in the level of a pegged exchange rate
	NAFTA	H	A common currency adopted in 1999 by 11 of the 15 countries of the European Union
	Countervailing Tariff	I	Groups of countries that have made trade agreements among themselves outside of the WTO
	European Union	J	An international agency established to oversee and maintain the system of pegged exchange rates set up in 1945.

Macro Chapter 12

Canada in the Global Economy

This chapter expands on a problem discussed in an earlier chapter: the international competitiveness of the manufacturing sector of the Canadian economy. The tariff protection which fostered the development of Canada's manufacturing sector has had two side-effects: (1) much of Canada's manufacturing industry is foreign-owned, consisting of "branch-plant" operations, and (2) Canadian manufacturing operations tend to be relatively small-scale. Both factors contribute to the difficulties of competing internationally.

While most of the public discussion of this matter tends to focus on the largely emotional issue of foreign ownership, the more serious concern is the economic issue of the performance of Canadian manufacturing, particularly its long-term future in the face of foreign competition.

The issue is what to do about this problem. The nationalistic approach does not appear particularly realistic without large-scale energy developments to use as the trade-off in bargaining with other nations; furthermore, Canada is not the only source of such resource products. Although the internationalist approach appeared threatening to many Canadian workers, especially in Ontario and Quebec's secondary manufacturing sectors, the Canadian government ratified a Free Trade Agreement with the United States on January 1, 1989. Then, in 1994, Canada, the United States and Mexico entered into the North American Free Trade Agreement (NAFTA) creating the world's largest free trade zone.

The politics of international trade caught up with the reality of economics. To compete, Canada was forced to turn its attention from the national perspective to the global market.

General Learning Objective

Examine the economic effects of Canadian international trade and investment policy, from the British policy of preferential tariffs in the 1800s to the current free trade agreement with the United States and Mexico.

Specific Learning Objectives

		Self-Test Reference
1.	Consider the National Policy of 1879 and the resulting effects of tariff protection on Canadian industry	#1-6
2.	Assess the reasons and consequences of Canada's lack of international competitiveness	#7-11
3.	Recognize the main tenets of the Canada-US trade agreement	#12
4.	Apply the Canadian strategies for success in the global economy	#13, 14
5.	Assess the Canada-US free trade agreement	#15,16
6.	Examine the characteristics of the Mexican economy and NAFTA	#17
	Address the question of foreign investment in Canada	#18-24
8.	Recognize the key terms used in this chapter	#25

Self-Test

1. The National Policy of 1879 was designed to protect which segment of the Canadian economy? _____

2. As a result of Canada's early high tariff policy, the Canadian manufacturing sector became _____ (smaller, larger) in size, foreign ownership of Canadian manufacturing _____ (increased, decreased) and the Canadian manufacturing sector became _____ (more, less) efficient.

3. Under the National Policy, foreign companies that desired to sell in Canada could avoid the higher Canadian tariffs by _____.

4. As a result of the move toward smaller "branch plant" firms and the reality of a smaller Canadian market for goods, determine if the following are TRUE or FALSE.

    _____ (a)   Manufacturing benefited from "economies of scale."

    _____ (b)   Average costs per unit were relatively higher than in the United States.

    _____ (c)   Canadian consumers had to subsidize the manufacturing industry by paying relatively higher prices.

5. Indicate whether each of the following statements regarding the form of foreign investment in Canada is **TRUE** or **FALSE**.

    _____ (a)   Mega projects, especially hydroelectric projects, have been financed by foreigners through loans.

    _____ (b)   Equity investment is preferred to debt investment because Canadian businesses have a greater chance of maintaining control.

    _____ (c)   Foreign investment has resulted in takeovers, plant expansion or closure, and the export of primary resources.

    _____ (d)   Of late, foreign firms in Canada appear to be content to use Canadian-earned profits to expand operations rather than import capital from abroad.

6. A basic purpose of Canadian tariff policy has been to promote the development of the manufacturing sector of the Canadian economy. Another effect of this tariff policy has been to

    (a)   benefit Canadian consumers.

    (b)   make manufacturing in Canada more efficient.

    (c)   reduce foreign ownership and control of Canadian manufacturing.

    (d)   increase foreign ownership and control of Canadian manufacturing.

    (e)   increase competition generally in the Canadian economy.

7. In the late 1980s what four factors were putting pressure on Canada to change its traditional policy of protecting its manufacturing sector?

    (a)   _____

    (b)   _____

(c) _____

(d) _____

8. Numerous studies of the reasons for low Canadian productivity in manufacturing conclude that

(a) Canadian workers are lazy.

(b) Canada is less endowed with natural resources compared to other industrialized countries.

(c) the small size of the Canadian market has prevented economies of scale.

(d) Canada's tariff policy has provided competitive protection for Canadian firms.

(e) both (c) and (d) are correct.

9. Other reasons cited for Canada's poor productivity performance are

(a) a short-term cost cutting philosophy as opposed to long-term strategic planning.

(b) managers who are slow to develop and adapt new technology.

(c) low research and development spending by Canadian companies.

(d) a relatively large proportion of low skilled workers who are often difficult to train.

(e) all of the above.

10. The free trade agreement between the United States and Canada was

(a) a major change, since tariffs between the two countries were very high.

(b) a much better deal for the United States than Canada.

(c) only the first part of a much broader strategy for the United States.

(d) not a major breakthrough because tariffs between the two countries had been coming down for decades.

(e) both (c) and (d).

11. The following factors of Column I forced Canada to move toward a newer trade policy. Choose the best choice from Column II that illustrates the effect of each of the factors. (Note that all of the choices of Column II fit somewhere in Column I.)

Column I

_____ (a)   Declining competitiveness

_____ (b)   Higher costs to Canadian consumers and exporters

_____ (c)   Outflows of investment capital

_____ (d)   Weaker markets for resources

_____ (e)   Growing protectionism in the United States

Column II

(1)   The Canadian company, Hudson Bay Mining and Smelting, invests in a new copper mine in Chile.

(2)   Americans levy duties on softwood lumber.

(3)   The cost of saving one job in Canada through protective measures rises from $25 000 to $200 000.

(4)   Lower cost foreign producers gain pulp and paper markets at the expense of Canadian firms.

(5)   Declining world demand causes lower sales for Canadian iron ore producers.

(6)   Retaliatory measures by foreigners result from Canadian protection of our beer and wine industry.

12.   With respect to the Canada-US Free Trade Agreement of 1989, are the following statements **TRUE** or **FALSE**?

_____ (a)   All tariffs between the two countries were to be removed immediately.

_____ (b)   Appeals of policy are handled by a neutral panel of five members.

_____ (c)   In times of energy shortages, Canada would be able to look after itself first and discriminate against US markets if necessary.

_____ (d)   The definition of a subsidy was too complex to solve under the initial trade agreement.

_____ (e)   Tariffs on heavily protected Canadian consumer goods would he phased out gradually over a ten year period.

13.   An automobile company decides to produce the "Trail Blazer" truck in Canadian plants. These plants provide the R & D, design, marketing, production and export for a world market. This strategy for success is known as

   (a)   niche marketing

   (b)   economies of scope

   (c)   world product mandating

   (d)   countervailing marketing

   (e)   total quality management

14.   The Tilley Co. provides a specialized clothing product in a unique fashion to North American consumers. This strategy for success is an example of

   (a)   niche marketing

   (b)   economies of scale

   (c)   world product mandating

   (d)   countervailing marketing

   (e)   direct marketing

15.   From Canada's perspective, success of the Canada-US trade deal can be measured by

   (a)   increased direct investment by foreigners in Canada.

   (b)   an improvement in Canadian export sales to the US.

   (c)   more disputes regarding the imposition of countervailing duties by the United States.

   (d)   both (a) and (b),

   (e)   none of the above.

16.   **True** or **False?** Canada has freer trade with the United States than between its own provinces.

17.   Are the following statements **TRUE** or **FALSE** regarding the Mexican economy?

   _____ (a)   Much of Mexican industry was either government owned or heavily regulated.

   _____ (b)   Mexico missed out on the resource boom, especially in oil, of the early 1980s.

_____ (c)   Mexico moved from an outward-looking market-oriented country to an inward-looking protected and regulated economy.

_____ (d)   In addition to NAFTA, Mexico entered a regional free trade agreement with central American countries in 1997.

18.   With respect to the economic impact of NAFTA on Canada

(a)   the potential gains were likely to be small due to Canada's smaller trade with Mexico and the fact that Canadians already had a trade agreement with the US.

(b)   only 15% of goods imported from Mexico to Canada were tariff-free, so free trade would greatly enhance the flow of goods.

(c)   Mexican productivity was higher than Canadian productivity — a factor that would be detrimental to the Canadian economy.

(d)   NAFTA would decrease export opportunities for a number of Canadian industries, especially in telecommunications, engineering and construction.

(e)   there appeared to be few strategic benefits for Canada from joining the agreement.

19.   The predominant attitude of the Canadian government over the years toward foreign investment has been

(a)   neutral; the government has sought neither to encourage nor to discourage it.

(b)   favourable; the government has sought to encourage it.

(c)   selective; the government has sought to encourage debt investment by foreigners but discourage equity investment.

(d)   unfavourable; the government has sought to discourage it.

(e)   none of the above.

20.   State whether each of the following statements regarding the effects of foreign investment in Canada is TRUE or FALSE.

_____ (a)   Without foreign investment Canada's manufacturing sector would have grown much faster.

_____ (b)   Foreign investors brought their savings, know-how and technology to Canada.

_____ (c)   Foreign investment increases the value of the Canadian dollar and supplies Canadians with US dollars to purchase US imports.

_____ (d)   Foreign investment has substantially added to Canada's standard of living.

_____ (e)   Foreign investment in Canada has been accompanied by an increased outflow of interest and dividends from Canadians to foreigners.

21.   In 1992 Canada's foreign debt as a percentage of GDP was

(a)   very low by world standards.

(b)   the highest in the world.

(c)   almost as high as Italy's.

(d)   it did not exist because Canada is a net lender of funds to the rest of the world.

22.   The Foreign Investment Review Act (FIRA) acted to screen

(a)   all proposals for foreign investment in Canada.

(b)   any expansion within Canada by foreign firms already operating in Canada.

(c)   proposals for foreign takeovers of Canadian firms over a given size and the expansion into new businesses by foreign corporations.

(d)   foreign investment in certain "key sectors" of the Canadian economy, such as banking, publishing and communications.

(e)   any investments by foreign firms leading to control of Canadian firms.

23.   The National Energy Program was

(a)   very encouraging to foreign investment in Canada's energy sector.

(b)   the replacement of FIRA.

(c)   hostile to foreign control of Canada's energy sector.

(d)   none of the above.

24.   The two main reasons for the Canadian dollar's low value in 1999 were

(a)   _____

_____

_____

(b)   _____

_____

_____

25. Match the terms on the left with the descriptions on the right.

	Globalization	A	Canada-U.S agreement of 1854 that eliminated certain tariffs
	Dispute Panel	B	Free trade in the auto industry
	Reciprocity Treaty	C	1867 Canadian system of protective tariffs
	Niche Marketing	D	A movement away from national markets
	Protectionism	E	Loans through the purchase of bonds; no ownership
	Auto Pact	F	A neutral panel to arbitrate trade disputes
	Debt Investment	G	Producers design, manufacture, and market for the world
	Equity Investment	H	Purchase of shares in an organization; ownership
	National Policy	I	Discouraging trade through tariff and other barriers.
	World Product Mandating	J	Producers target specific sectors of a market

Macro Chapter 13

INTO THE FUTURE

During the late 1980s and into the 1990s, the world experienced a major increase in international trade. This, combined with increased competition and a significantly greater mobility of capital, brought about a "globalization" of world markets. As a consequence of these developments, Canada has had to rethink its role as an international player. The old strategy of relying on the extraction of rich natural resources and protecting an inefficient manufacturing industry was becoming incompatible with the new realities.

As part of the changing world order, third world countries, notably in Asia and Latin America, as well as in the emerging market economies of Eastern Europe, were rapidly acquiring industrial and technological expertise, enabling them to become tough, aggressive, and efficient new competitors in international markets.

Canada faced the options of either attempting to insulate and isolate itself from these new competitive forces, or adapting itself to a rapidly changing world. If the latter option were to be followed it was evident that new economic policies and new directions would be required.

General Learning Objective

Evaluate Canada's strategies for improving its competitive position in world markets.

Specific Learning Objectives

		Self-Test Reference
1.	Reflect on Canada's traditional reliance on a resource- based economy	#1-3
2.	Consider the requirements of globalization	#4-5

3.   Review the Canadian government's policies to increase our competitive

        position   #6-8

4.   Recognize the key terms used in this chapter   #9

Self-Test

1.   Canada's traditional source of economic prosperity was in the

       (a)   export of manufactured goods.

       (b)   export of natural resources

       (c)   inflow of foreign business capital investment.

       (d)   establishment of social welfare programs.

       (e)   (a) and (c) above.

2.   Traditionally, government policies have been focused on

       _____ wealth not on _____ wealth.

3.   Resource wealth mentality is a view that economic wealth is

       _____

       _____

4.   Which of the following factors contributed to globalization?

       (a)   lower tariffs

       (b)   improved technology

       (c)   better transportation systems

       (d)   more countries entering the global market

       (e)   all of the above

5.   Which of the following are TRUE and which are FALSE?

       _____ (a)   Canada was slow to respond to globalization pressures in the
                     1980s.

       _____ (b)   Canada's manufacturing sector has always been internationally
                     competitive.

       _____ (c)   There were high costs to Canadians from avoiding globalization.

       _____ (d)   The key attraction for business investment is cheap labour.

_____ (e)   It is advantageous for countries to provide a stable macroeconomic environment.

_____ (f)   Education and training systems are key strategic assets.

6.   Three changes in Canadian macroeconomic that occurred after the mid 1980s were _____

_____

_____

7.   Which of the following was used to meet the government's objective of increased productivity?

(a)   competition legislation

(b)   deregulation

(c)   reduction of subsidies

(d)   privatization

(e)   all of the above

8.   The 1990s were a period of

(a)   avoiding change

(b)   adjusting to change

(c)   protectionism

(d)   high inflation

(e)   low unemployment

9.: Match the terms on the left with the definitions on the right.

	Resource Wealth Mentality	A	Policies to reduce the extent of regulation of businesses by government with the intention of promoting efficiency through increased competition
	Distribution of Wealth	B	Government rules that effect or control the operations and practices of business.
	Regulation	C	The view that society's economic wealth is derived mainly from the sale of natural resources
	De-Regulation	D	Provision of assistance to individuals, businesses and regions

Macro Answers

Chapter 1

1.   (d)

2.   is not; it deals with the behaviour of people, which cannot be precisely analyzed or predicted.

3.   (c)

4.   (b)

5.   false

6.   false. Economics focuses on "what is," analyzing the consequences of "what could be," and leaving "what ought to be" to politicians. A discussion of positive, normative and empirical economics may follow.

7.   all skills, along with the ability to do mental work.

8.   it increases production per person (productivity), making higher living standards possible.

9.   productivity.

10.   (d)

11.   (d)

12.   the development of new technology — oil, natural gas or nuclear power.

13.   (a)

14.   (a)

15.   (d)

16.   Opportunity cost

17.   (e)

18.   (c)

19.   (a)   The manual method is more efficient.

manual: (4 x 8 x 15) + 70 + (10 x 25) = $800; Per unit: 800 ÷ 25 = $32.

mechanized: (2 x 8 x 15) + 70 + 290 + (10 x 25) = $850;

Per unit: 850 ÷ 25 = $34.

(b)   The mechanized method is more efficient.

manual: (4 x 8 x 20) + 70 (10 x 25) = $960; Per unit: 960 ÷ 25 = $38.40.

mechanized: (2 x 8 x 20) + 70 + (10 x 25) = $930.

(c)   The mechanized method is more efficient.

manual: $32 per unit.

mechanized: 790 ÷ 25 = $31.60 per unit.

(d)   The manual method is more efficient

manual: $32 per unit.

mechanized: 900 ÷ 25 = $36 per unit.

(e)   The mechanized method is more efficient.

manual: $32 per unit.

mechanized: (2 x 8 x 15) + 70 + (10 x 50) + 340 = $1150.

Per unit: 1150 ÷ 50 = $23.

20.   consumers, as they make their spending decisions in the marketplace.

21.   (d)

22.   (d)

23.   lowering the price of the product and the profits of the producers, thus reducing the incentive to produce that product.

24.   (d)

25.   (a)   true   (d)   true   (g)   false

(b)   true   (e)   false

(c)   false   (f)   false

26. $720/$12,000 = 6%

27.   (a)   true   (c)   false

(b)   true   (d)   true

28.   (a) $5000

(b) $3750

(c) $5,000/$60,000 = 8.33%

(d) $1250 + $2750 + $1000 = $5000

29.   Governments (1) provides services to the public (2) regulate the operations and practices of business (3) redistribute incomes.

30. O   Economic resources

     H   Economic input

     K   Labour

     G   Capital equipment

     E   Return on investment

     M   Living standard

     Q   Land

     I   Output

     P   Scarcity

     T   Opportunity cost

     A   Effectiveness

     R   Efficiency

     N   Market system

     L   Profit

     S   Market power

     B   Recession

     D   Subsidy

     C   Gross domestic product

     J   Income distribution

     F   Mixed economic system

Chapter 2

1.   (a)   micro   (d)   macro

     (b)   micro   (e)   micro

     (c)   macro   (f)   macro

2.   (a)   the higher the skill level of the labour force, the greater the productivity of labour. High productivity allows for higher output of goods and services, and at lower cost.

     (b)   quantity and quality of capital equipment are important factors in determining the productivity of labour.

Macro Answers

     (c)   profit motive provides an incentive for business owners to produce efficiently.

3.   (d)

4.   aggregate demand

5.   (e)

6.   (a)   a high level of output, at or near the economy's potential output.

     (b)   ideally, should be at a high level, so that all members of the labour force are fully employed.

     (c)   should be at a low level (close to zero).

7.   the value of all final goods and services produced in a country during a year.

8.   (a)   consumption   (c)   government

     (b)   investment   (d)   Foreign (imports and exports) sector.

9.   (a)   government   (e)   investment

     (b)   imports   (f)   consumption

     (c)   investment   (g)   exports

     (d)   exports   (h)   investment

10. $260 000

11. $220 billion.

12. $30 billion.

13. $430 billion.

14.   prices that prevailed during the year in which GDP was measured.

15.   is calculated using prices that prevailed during the "base year."

16.   price increases have exceeded the increases in real output.

17.   underground economic activity, the standard of living, the quality of life.

18.   (a)   GDP is an estimate of the grand total output of (final) goods and services of the Canadian economy in that year.

     (b)   No. If the prices of goods and services increased, then some of that 6% increase in GDP would represent price increases. Suppose the price increases were 2.5% — if we deduct the price increase of 2.5% from the 6.0%, then the output of goods and services ("Real GDP") would have risen by 3.5% (6.0 – 2.5).

19. (a) (1) 97.8 (4) 565

 (2) 506 (5) 674

 (3) 109.6 (6) 750

 (b) (570-506)/506 times 100% = 12.6%; (124.9-100)/100*100% = 24.9%

 (c) rose, (506-478)/478 times 100% = 5.9%; rose, (506-489)/489 times

 100% = 3.5%; rose, (100-97.8)/97.8 times 100% = 2.2%.

20. the annual rate of increase in the general price level.

21. reference to the consumer price index: the annual increase in the CPI.

22. the average of the prices of goods and services bought by representative urban

 households.

23. (143.8-138.2)/138.2 times 100% = 4.1%

24. (127.2 times 4%) + 127.2 = 132.3

25. the number of unemployed people expressed as a percentage of the labour force.

26. (1 167 000 / (12 000 000 + 1 167 000)) times 100% = 8.86%

27. (a) 13.797 – 12.240 = 1.557; (b) 13.945; (c) 1.562

 Calculate the solutions to (b) and (c) using the following formula:

 Unemployment rate = (number unemployed (U))/ (number employed (E) +

 unemployed (U)). Therefore:

 11.2% = U / (12.383 + U), and 11.2% is the same as 0.112. Therefore:

 U = .112 (12.383 + U) = .112 times 12.383 + .112 times U. Therefore:

 1 times U - .112 times U = .112 times 12.383, so .888 times U = 1.387, and

 U = 1.387 / .888 = 1.562 (solution to (c). Labor force (b) = 12.383 + 1.562 =

 13.945.

28. (a) From a survey of Canadian households that is conducted each month.

 (b) 13 200 000 (22 000 000 x .60)

 (c) 1 000 000 (13 200 000 – 12 200 000)

 (d) 7.6% (1 000 000/13 200 000)

29. (a) structural;

 (b) structural

 (c) frictional

 (d) seasonal

(e)   cyclical

(f)   none of the above. This would be an example of involuntary or "hidden" unemployment. However, this person (though partially unemployed) would be "officially" employed.

30.   C frictional; A seasonal; B cyclical; E structural; D hidden.

31.   (d)

32.   (a)

33.   (d)

34.   L   Microeconomics

        F   Macroeconomics

        G   Demand side of the economy

        J   Supply side of the economy

        O   Aggregate demand

        H   Inflation

        B   Capacity output

        A   Full employment

        D   Gross domestic product

        I   Net exports

        P   Real income

        E   Money GDP

        C   Real GDP

        K   CPI

        Q   Labour participation rate

        M   Labour force

        N   Unemployed person

Chapter 3

1.   (d)

2.   the amount and quality of capital equipment per worker (and therefore, the amount of capital investment undertaken by society)

3.   (c)

4. (d)

5. (a)

6. (c)

7. lower, higher

8. (d)

9. Wealthy countries find it relatively easy to forgo consumption (save) in order to invest and grow; poor countries cannot afford to give up present consumption in order to save and invest in capital goods which would facilitate economic growth.

10. (a) British enterprise paid low rates, forcing low consumption upon workers, and invested their profits back into their businesses.

    (b) The Soviet state diverted resources away from the production of consumer goods (thus forcing the people to save), and used these resources to produce capital goods.

11. (a) Education and skill levels of the labour force.

    (b) The level of managerial ability.

    (c) Size of the market and scale of operations, which provides opportunities for increased specialization.

    (d) Incentives in the economic system that promote efficiency.

    (e) The state of the economy, i.e., rising production, generates higher worker productivity.

12.

Income	Income Tax	Average Tax Rate	Marginal Tax Rate
$30 000	$5000	16.7% (5000/30 000)	
31 000	5300	17.1% (5300/31 000)	30.0% (300/1000)
32 000	5650	17.7% (5650/32 000)	35.0% (350/1000)
33 000	6050	18.3% (6050/33 000)	40.0% (400/1000)

13. 25

14. 25, 21.9

    An increase in the average or marginal tax rate might reduce Carol's incentive to work extra time. She might save less with higher tax rates; however, since her disposable income also rises, she will likely same more.

15. increased efficiency as a result of larger-scale productive operations.

16. (d)

17. (b)

18. (d)

19. (d)

20. (d)

21. Widening; 88; 68

22. hiring workers; adding capital equipment

23. industrial structure, plant size

24. The major productivity increases have been in the high tech sector, which comprises a much larger portion of U.S. manufacturing than it does in Canada. Therefore the impact of total U.S. productivity is much greater.

25. 1. Tax incentives to save (e.g. RRSP's).

2. Encouraging education and training.

3. Encouraging managers to focus on exports.

4. Negotiating trade agreements with other countries.

5. Reducing capital taxes to encourage investment.

26. It would increase productivity, due to:

(a) increased foreign competition that would push Canadian firms to become more efficient, and

(b) Canadian producers would have access to larger foreign markets, which would allow them to enjoy greater economies of scale than are possible in the small Canadian market.

27. the relationship between the level of total output and the cost per unit of producing that output.

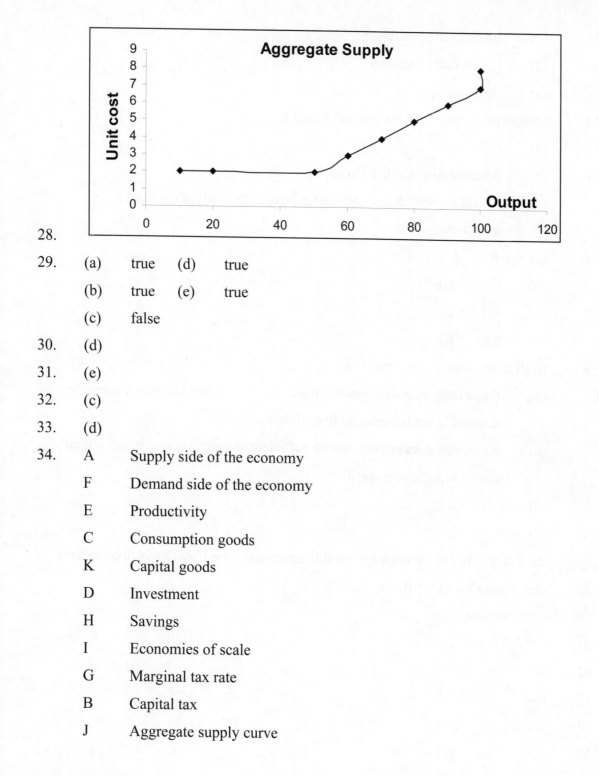

28.

29. (a)   true   (d)   true

     (b)   true   (e)   true

     (c)   false

30. (d)

31. (e)

32. (c)

33. (d)

34.   A   Supply side of the economy

     F   Demand side of the economy

     E   Productivity

     C   Consumption goods

     K   Capital goods

     D   Investment

     H   Savings

     I   Economies of scale

     G   Marginal tax rate

     B   Capital tax

     J   Aggregate supply curve

Chapter 4

1. total spending on goods and services. The four components:

     (1)   consumption spending

Macro Answers

      (2)   investment spending

      (3)   government spending

      (4)   net exports

2.   consumption spending; investment spending

3.   (a)   60%

      (b)   personal disposable income

      (c)   consumer confidence and interest rates (the level of consumer indebtedness, too)

4.   (a)   10-12%

      (b)   (i)   fall

             (ii)   rise

             (iii) fall

5.   Both statements are incorrect:

      (a)   Since total income payments equal the value of production, aggregate demand is not necessarily insufficient.

      (b)   Aggregate demand will not be sufficient to purchase maximum output if not all incomes are spent.

6.   (d)

7.   (c)

8.   the funds saved are invested in capital equipment which increases productivity.

9.   down; paradox of thrift.

10.   remain stable

11.   fall

12.   (e)

13.   rise

14.   (b)

15.   (a) fall (c) fall

      (b) rise (d) rise

16.   (a) fall; be depressed (c) equal

      (b) rise; expand

17.   (a) increase (d) increase

(b)   increase   (e)   increase

(c)   decrease   (f)   increase

18.   The inflation may have been avoided if aggregate supply had also increased (i.e., shifted to the right).

19.   (a)   Aggregate demand would begin to increase as consumer spending began to rise. With interest rate lower and the economic outlook better, consumers would be more inclined to borrow to buy "big-ticket" items. The lower interest rates may also induce some businesses to spend on capital investment projects.

       (b)   (i)   Output would increase. Producers are operating below capacity, so will be able to increase output in response to the rising demand.

               (ii)   Employment would increase as producers would need more employees to increase production. As employment grew, unemployment would fall.

               (iii)   The rate of inflation would not probably not increase by much, and maybe not at all. While aggregate demand is higher, producers will be able to increase output (supply) due to the fact that they are operating below capacity output.

20.   (a)   false   (d)   false

       (b)   true   (e)   true

       (c)   true   (f)   true

21.   (a)

22.   (e)

23.   H   Demand side of the economy

       L   Aggregate demand

       K   Consumption spending

       F   Personal disposable income

       I   Consumer confidence

       J   Interest rate

       C   Consumer indebtedness

       B   Personal saving

E	Personal saving rate
M	Business savings
D	Retained earnings
G	Capacity output
A	Inflation

Chapter 5

1.   it influences the level of aggregate demand.

2.   recession; inflation

3.   (a)   medium of exchange

      (b)   a standard of value

      (c)   store of value

4.   (a)   a store of value

      (b)   medium of exchange

      (c)   a store of value

      (d)   medium of exchange

      (e)   a standard of value

5.   (c)

6.   divisible, durable, scarce, portable.

7.   (a) true   (d)   false

      (b) true   (e)   true

      (c) false

8.   (a) true   (d)   true

      (b) false   (e)   false

      (c) false

9.   (a) false   (d)   false

      (b) true   (e)   false

      (c) true

10.   (e)

11.   (a) neither (g)   neither

      (b) neither (h)   money

(c)   money (i)   neither

(d)   money (j)   near-money

(e)   neither (k)   neither

(f)   money

12.   5-8,92-95

13.   13.   (a)   true   (d)   false

                (b)   true   (e)   true

                (c)   true

14.   currency (notes and coins) outside the banks plus demand deposits.

15.   (e)

16.   deposits at trust and mortgage loan companies, credit unions and caisses populaires.

17.   (a) $25 billion   (c) $162 billion

        (b) $105 billion

18.   (e)

19.   M2 or M2+

20.   bank deposits; the lending activities of the banking system.

21.   (d)

22. $1.9 million

23.   decrease

24.   increase, decrease. Most transactions are by cheque so cash withdrawals are unnecessary.

25. $95 000, $5000, $95 000, $90 250, $4750, $2 million (i.e., 20 x 100 000).

26.   (a)   remains the same

        (b)   decreases

        (c)   remains the same

        (d)   remains the same

        (e)   increases

        (f)   increases

27.   (d)

28.   (d)

29. In good times banks lend more and increase the money supply, which may result in too much money chasing too few goods, i.e., inflation.

30. inflation, recession.

31. E   Money Supply

      C   M1

      D   M2

      F   M2+

      A   Cash Reserve

      B   Cash Reserve Ratio

Chapter 6

1. (a) contraction   (c) peak

      (b) expansion   (d) trough

2. (b)

3. fluctuations and aggregate demand

4. (e)

5. (c)

6. (a)

7. the fraction of changes in income which is respent.

8. imports, taxes, and savings.

9. 1.67

10. (b)

11. (b)

12. 1.6

13. (a) 1.5

      (b) Initial investment spending: $9 million

           Stage 1 of respending: $3 million

           Stage 2 of respending: $1 million

           Total change in income (end of stage 2): $13 million

           Total change in income (end of series): $13.5 million

      (c) $22.5 million

14. (d)

15. the economy must be at or near capacity output.

16. capital investment undertaken by business in response to increases in sales (which have brought production to near-capacity levels) and which are expected to continue.

17. keep rising

18. fall

19. $3 million; $9 million; $6 million.

20. (e)

21. $160 million; $240 million.

22. (a) & (b)

Year	Capital	Investment
993	37.5	7.5
994	50	12.5

(c) $50 million; 0

(d) 1993: expansion

1994: expansion

1995: recession

23.

	Investment	Change in Income
1993	$7.5	$15
1994	12.5	25
1995	0	0

24. (d)

25. (a) yes   (d) yes

(b) yes   (e) no

(c) yes

26. (a) yes   (d) no

(b) yes   (e) yes

(c) yes

27. (e)

28. (a) This is a profile of an economy in which there is a very high level of aggregate demand — an economic boom with high levels of confidence

and borrowing that are generating a strong interaction between the multiplier and accelerator effects. Note that the question states that the unemployment rate is not only very low, but also still falling, which indicates that the economy has not yet "peaked."

(b) The major problem would be *inflation* — if unemployment is that low, the economy has to be near its capacity level of output.

(c) Higher inflation would bring higher interest rates. In order to protect the value (purchasing power) of their funds against inflation, lenders would require higher rates of interest.

(d) The logical expectation would be a downturn. In such an economy, high and rising inflation would generate very high interest rates that would eventually overcome the optimism and curtail borrowing, setting the stage for a downturn. It is very unlikely that the boom will continue — with the unemployment rate already the lowest it has been in a decade, a downturn should be expected fairly soon.

29. (1) By forecasting the various components of aggregate demand, using past trends and likely future developments.

(2) By using leading economic indicators, which tend to rise or fall before the GDP shows any appreciable change.

30. B Business Cycle

A Boom

G Multiplier

C Accelerator

D Induced Investment

E Inflation Psychology

H Recession Psychology

F Leading Economic Indicator

Chapter 7

1. (d)

2. (a) true (d) false

    (b)   true   (e)   false

    (c)   true   (f)   false

3.   a privately-owned, financial intermediary chartered by an Act of Parliament.

4.   (c)

5.   the federal government; to regulate the money supply and interest rates.

6.   fall by $20 million; decline; rise; decline by $20 million; remain the same.

7.   tighter.

8.   easy; increase; reduce.

9.   buying; lowering; into

10.   (d)

11.   (b)

12.   (b)

13.   increasing the federal government's deposits (book entries) at the Bank of Canada.

14.   increase; increase; remain the same; remain the same.

15.   (c)

16.   (a) true (d) true

    (b) true (e) true

    (c) true

17.   (e)

18.   (d)

19.   increase

20.   (e)

21.   depress

22.   (b)

23.   neutral

24.   (a) no (e) no

    (b) yes (f) yes

    (c) no (g) yes

    (d) yes

25.   (d)

26.   Counter cyclical fiscal policy involves the use of government budget deficits to stimulate aggregate demand during a recession, and government budget surpluses to reduce aggregate demand during an inflationary period.

27.   (a)   yes   (c)   no

        (b)   no   (d)   yes

28.   rise by $112 million

29.   (b)

30.   severe inflation, as the extra money gets into circulation and gets spent, causing an increase in aggregate demand.

31.   the overall debt of the federal government: the difference between the federal government's liabilities and its net recorded assets (mostly those assets which yield interest, profits, or dividends).

32.   The National Debt is the total accumulation of federal government deficits, less any repayments made in periods when the federal budget is in a surplus position.

33.   (a)   yes   (d)   yes

        (b)   no   (e)   yes

        (c)   no

34.   (a)   false   (g)   true

        (b)   true   (h)   true

        (c)   false   (i)   false

        (d)   false   (j)   true

        (e)   true   (k)   true

        (f)   false

35.   (1)   rising interest rates, which make capital investment less predictable

        (2)   the "crowding out effect," where government borrowing leaves insufficient funds for private business borrowing

36.   (a)

37.   (d)

38.   (d)

39.   upward; increase; higher; increase; major; compound

40.

Recessions:

(a) Monetary Policy:

An *"easy money"* policy which would cause interest rates to *fall*.

(b) Fiscal Policy:

A government budget *deficit*, with government spending *greater than* its tax revenues.

(c) How these Policies Work:

(a) and (b) will shorten the recession by *increasing aggregate demand in the economy*.

(d) Side-Effects of Policies:

If used too strongly, the policies in (a) and (b) may cause *inflation*, if they *increase aggregate demand too much*.

Periods of boom/inflation:

(a) Monetary Policy:

A *"tight money"* policy which would cause interest rates to *rise*.

(b) Fiscal Policy:

A government budget *surplus*, with government spending *smaller than* its tax revenues.

(c) How these Policies Work:

(a) and (b) will reduce the rate of inflation by *reducing aggregate demand in the economy*.

(d) Side-Effects of Policies:

The policies in (a) and (b) will cause *higher unemployment* because they *reduce aggregate demand in the economy*.

41.   (1)   Interest payments (a major expenditure) must be made

      (2)   Social programs (also a major expenditure) are politically difficult to cut back

42.   (c)

43.   C   Treasury Bill

      D   Easy Money Policy

      F   Tight Money Policy

      A   Prime Rate

      B   Fiscal Policy

      E   Automatic Stabilizer

      H   Budget Deficit

      G   Balanced Budet

Chapter 8

1. structural

2. unemployment rates are highest among young people (age 15-24) and in Quebec and the coastal regions of Canada.

3. Yes, in the short run, but in the long run if a firm is successful growth through increased sales can actually result in more employment.

4. a higher standard of living will result in higher aggregate demand; an increase in international competitiveness will increase exports.

5. if workers are replaced by capital the demand for labour will decrease

6. (b)

7. (c)

8. (b)

9. less; more

10. (d)

11. pursue one economic goal through a course of action which will have a negative effect on the achievement of at least one other economic goal.

12. increased inflation

13. the lowest attainable unemployment rate

14. Canada has a high labour force participation rate which may contribute to the high unemployment rate

15. (a) create more jobs; improve skills of workers; improve incentives of workers

    (b) improving the skills of workers will eliminate the skill mismatch and reduce structural unemployment

16. (a) The "recognition lag" due to the time it takes for the authorities to recognize the existence of a particular economic problem.

    (b) The "policy lag," before the appropriate economic policies can be implemented.

    (c) The "impact lag," before these policies have an effect on the economy.

17. (a) false   (d) true

(b) true   (e)   true

(c) false (f)   true

18. Canada is unable to lower interest rates without generating an outflow of foreign funds. The high Canadian debt means interest rates must be attractive to foreigners.

19. (a) likely   (d)   likely

(b) not likely (e)   likely

(c) likely

20. (a) likely   (c)   likely

(b) not likely (d)   likely

21. Credit downgrades due to the substantial Canadian debt held by foreigners has forced the government to act to reduce their deficit. A rise in taxes may result in an outflow of foreign investment so the government is left with little choice but to reduce spending.

22. (a) economic growth

(b) full employment

(c) stable prices

23. stable prices

24. the high levels of aggregate demand, which generate economic growth and full employment, also tend to generate inflation.

25   D   Employment to population Ratio

C   Capacity Output

B   Budget Surplus

G   Recognition Lag

F   Time Lag

I   Impact Lag

A   Cyclical Unemployment

H   Policy Lag

E   Full employment

Chapter 9

1.   (a)

2.   (b)

3.   (d)

4.   import quotas, licenses, preferential purchasing policies, subsidies, voluntary export restraints, rules and procedures

5.   telecommunication equipment, comparative advantage

6.   (e)

7.   (c), (b), (a), (d)

8.   specialization, increased competition and economies of scale.

9.   The theory of comparative advantage.

10. (a)

	Canadian Firm	Chinese Firm
Hourly costs	$90	$10
Hourly output	3000	200
Cost per unit	$90 ÷ 3000 = $.03	$10 ÷ 200 = $.05

   (b) $ per unit

   (c)   technologically advanced capital equipment

   (d) $100 000 in China

   (e) $60 000 in Canada

11. False, because technological advancement and higher productivity in many North American industries result in lower costs per unit of output despite the higher wage rates in North America.

12. False. Efficient and competitive producers, such as agricultural and primary product industries (as well as some manufacturers) favour freer trade, which would allow them freer access to foreign markets.

13. (b)

14. (a)   120 000

   (b)   80 000

   (c)   120 000 - 80 000 = 40 000

   (d)   zero, since free trade without tariffs is assumed.

   (e)   105 000

(f)   95 000

(g)   105 000 - 95 000 = 10 000

(h)   10 000 ¥ $10 = $100 000 per month

(i)   — Consumers lose because they now pay a higher price and there is a reduction in the purchases of the product.

         — Foreign suppliers lose since they have less sales to Canadians.

         — Canadian importers suffer from the same plight as foreign suppliers (i.e., less sales and subsequently lower income).

         — Government gains as a result of the $100 000 tariff revenues and the higher tax revenues from Canadian producers. The government is likely to lose some income tax revenues from the Canadian importers since their employment and profits decline.

         — Canadian firms gain as a result of their improvement in sales.

(j)   A subsidy of $10 per unit to producers is a better way of isolating the cost of protection and eliminating the other side-effects of tariff protection.

15.   other nations will retaliate by increasing their tariffs on Canadian products. Consequently, some jobs will be "saved" in Canadian industries which receive increased tariff protection, while other jobs will be lost in industries which will suffer retaliatory tariff increases by foreign nations.

16.   (b)

17.   (a)   no   (e)   no

        (b)   no   (f)   yes

        (c)   yes   (g)   no

        (d)   yes   (h)   ho

18.   Smaller markets for Canadian producers, loss of sales and jobs in export industries as a result of retaliation by trading partners, and reduced competition for Canadian producers.

19.   (a)   false

        (b)   false

        (c)   false

        (d)   true

20. (b), (c), (d), (e)

21. (a)   provide considerable advance notice of tariff reductions

     (b)   provide financial and/or technical assistance to help firms adjust to the
            new situation

     (c)   provide retraining and/or relocation assistance to help workers adjust to
            the new situation

22. (a)

23. (e)

24. F   Subsidy

     D   Bureaucratic procedure

     E   Tariff

     A   Import quota

     B   Branch plant

     C   Comparative advantage theory

     G   Globalization

Chapter 10

1.   the price of one currency in terms of a foreign currency.

2. $1.16482 Canadian

3.   .522985 pounds

4.   (a)   increase

     (b)   decrease

     (c)   decrease

     (d)   increase

     (e)   decrease

     (f)   increase

     (g)   parts (a), (d) and (f) are appreciations, whereas (b), (c) and (e) are
            depreciations

5.   (d)

6.   rise or appreciate

7.   (a)   receipt   (e)   receipt

	(b)	payment	(f)	payment
	(c)	payment	(g)	payment
	(d)	payment	(h)	receipt

8. (a) surplus

   (b) deficit

   (c) depreciate; appreciate; demand

9. (a) (i) false   (iv) true

   (ii) true   (v) false

   (iii) false

   (b) deficit

   (c) fall or depreciate

   (d) Exporters, because our export goods and services are relatively cheaper as a result of the Canadian dollar depreciation.

   (e) Importers and consumers of imported goods, because these goods are now more expensive.

10. (a) Both of these factors involve payments to foreigners, causing deficit tendencies in the current account.

    (b) Tends to fall or depreciate as a result of (a).

    (c) They are now more expensive.

    (d) (i) buy Canadian dollars on the foreign exchange market and/or

        (ii) increase Canadian interest rates relative to foreign rates to attract foreign currency, thereby increasing the demand for Canadian dollars.

    (e) managed float or dirty float.

11. (d)

12. (e)

13. (d)

14. increase

15. increase; less.

16. (c)

17. (a)

18.   expansionary, fall, less, increase.

19.   (a)   Canadian pulp and paper companies are exporters and benefit from a depreciated Canadian dollar.

        (b)   as the dollar appreciates against foreign currencies, import prices decline.

        (c)   The bank is attempting to accomplish

            (i)   An orderly market for the Canadian dollar. The bank wishes to stabilize the currency to avoid wide swings in price.

            (ii)   The avoidance of a renewal of Canadian price inflation caused by higher import prices and followed by concomitant wage increases.

20.   (a) $11 000 000

            Since $1 Canadian = 200 yen

            1 yen = 1/200 = $.005

            Thus, one imported auto costs

            2.2 million x $.005 = $11 000

            1000 cars cost 1000 x $11 000 = $11 million

        (b)   15 714 286 (i.e., 1000 x 2.2 million x 1/140

        (c)   increase; decrease; automatic adjustment mechanism

21.   (a)   true   (d)   true

        (b)   false   (e)   false

        (c)   true

22.   (a)   false

        (b)   true

        (c)   true

23.   (a)   no   (d)   yes

        (b)   yes   (e)   yes

        (c)   yes   (f)   no

24.   (1)   Heavy borrowing by governments in foreign countries

        (2)   Relatively high interest rates

25.   (a)   buyer, decrease, American, selling, depreciation.

        (b)   the Bank of Canada has inadequate reserves of foreign exchange to cover the Canadian bonds held by foreigners. As of 1993, there were over $300 billion of Canadian bonds outstanding while the Bank of Canada held only $10 billion of foreign exchange reserves.

26. decline

27. (b)

28. Limiting

29. B   Exchange Rate

     A   Foreign Exchange Markets

     I   Balance of Payments

     E   current Account

     D   Capital Account

     G   Hot Money

     C   Balance of Payments Deficit

     J   Floating Exchange Rate

     F   Dirty Float

     H   Foreign Exchange Speculation

Chapter 11

1.   Protective tariffs and the manipulation of their currencies lower.

2.   Retaliation by another country with higher tariff barriers.

3.   Instability in currency values and less international trade.

4.   (b)

5.   (c)

6.   stagnate; increase.

7.   (c)

8.   The International Monetary Fund.

9.   GATT/WTO.

10. Tariff barriers, Non-tariff barriers.

11. (a)

12. (a)

13. (c)

14. (a)   no   (d)   no

(b)   no   (e)   no

(c)   yes

15. (a) Lend foreign exchange reserves and gold to the country.

(b) A change in economic policies by the country to reduce its balance of payments deficit.

16. Purchases and sales of foreign exchange reserves and gold.

17. Because the US economy was strong and its currency was backed by gold.

18. (e)

19. true, true, false, true

20. rise; sell; buy.

21. fall; buy; sell.

22. (d)

23. (c)

24. Economic conditions change over time. Some nations experience surpluses in their Balance of Payments pushing their exchanges rates upward. Other nations have deficits, causing their currencies to depreciate.

25. Devaluation.

26. It has evolved to promote exchange rate stability, and to meet the needs of developing countries by increasing its loan limits and extending its repayment periods.

27. (d)

28. (d)

29. (b)

30. more

31. sells; buys.

32. (a) Petro Dollars.

b) Unstable exchange rates.

c) Yes, the dirty float system of exchange rates offered the flexibility in dealing with such potential instability.

33. (c)

34. It involved such large flows of capital in and out of the affected countries, and involved banks and other corporations from around the world.

35. The conditions were bank reform, the elimination of government mega projects, the elimination of government budget deficits, and higher interest rates to stop inflation.

36. Capital flows.

37.
F	Trade War
C	G.A.T.T
A	W.T.O.
J	I.M.F.
I	Trading Blocks
G	Devaluation
H	Euro
B	N.A.F.T.A.
D	Countervailing tariff
E	European Union
A	Foreign Exchange Markets

Chapter 12

1. The manufacturing industry

2. larger, increased, less

3. building a subsidiary plant in Canada

4. (a) false (c) true
   (b) true

5. (a) true (c) true
   (b) false (d) true

6. (d)

7. (a) The declining competitiveness of Canadian industry

   (b) The growing costs to consumers and exporters of protecting uncompetitive manufacturers from competition.

   (c) Outflows of Canadian business investment capital.

	(d)	The growing protectionism of the United States.
8.	(e)	
9.	(e)	
10.	(e)	

11. (a) 4 (d) 5
     (b) 3 and 6(e) 2
     (c) 1

12. (1) false (4) true
     (2) true (5) true
     (3) false

13. (c)

14. (a)

14. (d)

16. True

17. (1) true (3) false
     (2) false (4) true

18. (a)

19. (b)

20. (a) false (d) true
     (b) true (e) true
     (c) true

21. (b)

22. (c)

23. (c)

24.. (a) Interest payments on Canada's massive foreign debt, which generated outflows of $30 billion per year.

      (b) Low productivity of Canadian industry, which could only compete internationally with the assistance of a low valued currency.

25.   D Globalization
      F Disputes panel
      A Reciprocity treaty

J   Niche marketing

I   Protectionism

B   Auto Pact

E   Debt investment

H   Equity investment

C   National Policy

G   World product mandating

Chapter 13

1.   (e)

2.   distributing, creating

3.   something that occurs through possessing and selling resources

4.   (e)

5.   (a)   true   (d)   false

         (b)   false   (e)   true

         (c)   true   (f)   false

6.   freer trade through tariff elimination, reduction of inflation through tighter monetary policy, reduction of deficits through spending cuts

7.   (e)

8.   (b)

9.   C   Resource Wealth Mentality

         B   Regulation

         D   Distribution of Wealth

         A   De-Regulation